A TUTTLE TWINS SERIES OF STORIES
AMERICA'S HISTORY
1215-1776

This book is dedicated to
Murray Rothbard.

For looking at history
through a lens of liberty.

ISBN 978-1-943521-94-4

Boyack, Connor, author.
Stanfield, Elijah, illustrator.
America's History: A Tuttle Twins Series of Stories, volume 1 (1215-1776) / Connor Boyack.

Cover design by Elijah Stanfield
Chapter title illustrations by Sergio Cariello
Edited and typeset by Connor Boyack

Printed in Canada

A TUTTLE TWINS SERIES OF STORIES

AMERICA'S HISTORY

1215-1776

Connor Boyack and Elijah Stanfield

Table of Contents

Why Another History Book?

A simple conversation can spark a new idea.

That's what happened to me recently. I was chatting with some friends about American history and how effectively children today are being taught about our country's past. We all agreed that there were problems, but no one seemed to be focused on a solution.

But before you can identify the solution, it's important to truly understand your problem. So after that conversation, I bought a dozen social studies books—the popular ones used to teach American history in schools all across the country. When they had all arrived, I spent the day going through each one to see how well I felt they were teaching our history.

I was blown away—and not in a good way. While all of these books taught the names, dates, and events, they all consistently failed in two major ways:

1. None of the books taught about the *ideas* that led to America's founding. Sure, they all talked about how colonists were upset about taxation without representation in Parliament... but that's just one piece of a much larger puzzle! None of these books really covered the different ideas, philosophies, and influences that led the colonists to pick a fight with the world's greatest superpower. How can we really understand the events of the revolution without getting a peek into the minds of those who started it?

2. These books taught the factoids of history, but none of them explained why kids today should care about any of it. They didn't even attempt to make history relatable to our modern day, or give examples of why history should matter to kids. If we're supposed to learn *from* the past—not just *about* the past—then you would think these books would help students do that. They didn't!

This book you're holding is our solution to these problems. It's our attempt to teach not just the *what* of history, but also the *why*—because it's those ideas that we can relate to and learn from in our complex, modern world.

As you'll soon see, our first story begins long before the Revolution. We start by looking at international trade and how people pursuing personal happiness soon began to think about personal freedom—not just for kings and popes, but for all people, no matter where they lived or what they looked like. It was a new set of ideas that spread throughout society and led to a huge battle between power and freedom.

It's a story that's worth telling. Ready to dive in?

Connor Boyack

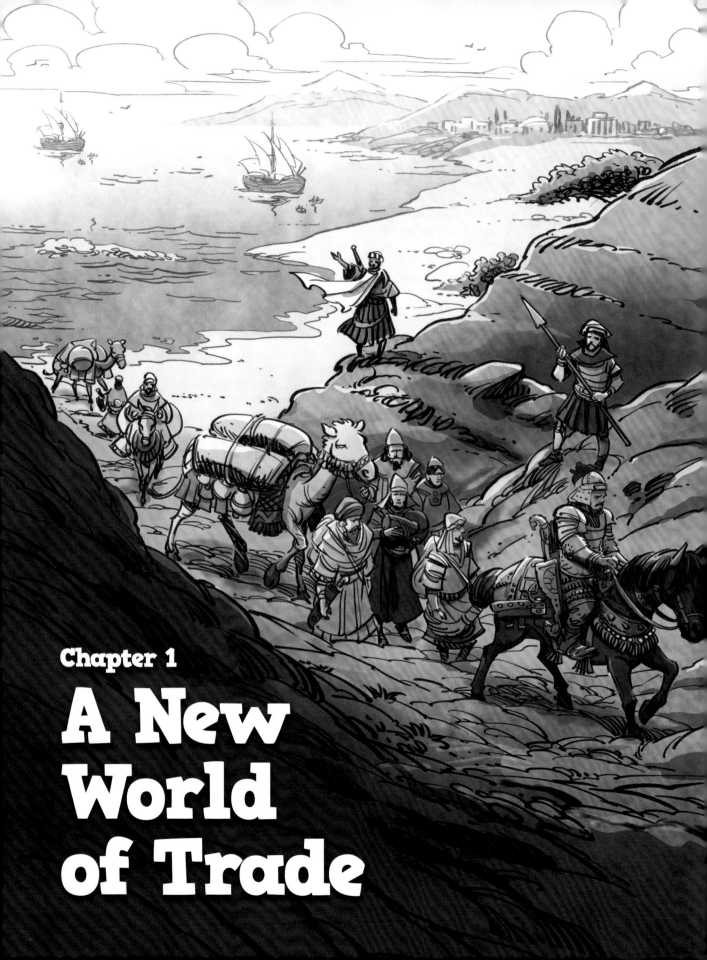

Chapter 1
A New World of Trade

Marco Polo & the Silk Road

The clear, blue sky hung like a curtain from the trees on both sides of the pool. Parents read books or tapped on their phones while their kids played under the eagle eyes of the lifeguard. The sun beat down hard, but that was okay. The water was cool and all the kids loved it, diving and splashing and calling out to one another. "Marco!" shouted a boy with his eyes shut tight, leaping at anyone who made a sound.

"Polo!" the others called back.

Just when the game was getting good, the lifeguard blew her whistle. "Lifeguard swap! Kids out of the pool for five minutes!" She didn't react when twenty kids let out a huge "Aaawwwww!" and reluctantly exited the pool.

Mrs. Tuttle sat reading at the side of the pool on a lounge chair. Her twin children, Ethan and Emily, came over and picked up their towels. No matter how hot the sun was, it was a little chilly getting out of the water.

"That's a fun game you were playing," Mrs. Tuttle said.

"Marco Polo is totally fun," Ethan said. "But I wonder why we call it 'Marco Polo'. It's just tag, isn't it?"

"Except it's in the pool and whoever is 'it' has their eyes closed," Emily said. "But I don't know why it's called that, either."

Mrs. Tuttle laughed. "It's been that way since long before you were born. We used to play Marco Polo when I was your age. Your dad looked it up once; it turns out *nobody* knows why we call it that. But we do know who Marco Polo was."

"Did he go swimming a lot?" Emily asked.

Mrs. Tuttle laughed again, and put her bookmark in her book. "Maybe. He was an Italian explorer."

"Cool," Ethan said, lying on his towel on the warm pool deck and letting the sun bake him.

"And a successful businessman—a merchant," Mrs. Tuttle said. "He took one of the longest journeys a person could take in those days, going all the way from Italy to China and back. That trade route is called the Silk Road."

Ethan's stomach growled. "Speaking of China, can we have those Chinese noodles you make for dinner?"

"Sure," she said. "I bet Marco Polo loved Chinese noodles, too. There were a lot of foods in China that you couldn't grow in Europe's climate. Fruits, warm-weather vegetables, and especially spices like pepper and cinnamon."

"I can't imagine a world without cinnamon..." Ethan said.

"We're spoiled, for sure," Mrs. Tuttle replied. "But spices were used for all kinds of things. Back then, before electricity and refrigerators, it was very difficult to keep food from spoiling. Spices helped preserve them, which improved the lives of Europeans greatly."

"There were other special things China had, like jade and silk. You could make a lot of money if you could get those things to the West to trade."

"I suppose that's why they called it the Silk Road?" Emily asked.

"Right. It was a long trip, and very dangerous," Mrs. Tuttle explained. "There were wild animals and treacherous landscapes. You could also be attacked by bandits, or arrested by kings who were uneasy about strangers coming through their countries."

"The 4,000 mile journey from Italy to China is wider than the whole United States. Many traders made that journey, but Marco wrote about it, and that's why he's famous."

"And also famous for being good at tag apparently," Ethan said.

"And swimming," Emily added.

The whistle blew. "You better get back in the water yourselves," Mrs. Tuttle said. "We'll be going home soon."

More About Me!

Marco Polo
1254-1324

- Polo's book *The Travels of Marco Polo* provided Europeans with one of the first accounts of what life was like in Asia.

- During his 24-year adventure to lands thousands of miles away from his home, he encountered people of many different religions, including Muslims, Jews, Christians, Hindus, and Buddhists.

- Marco Polo spoke four different languages. The most beneficial was likely Turkish, which was spoken in many parts of Asia during his time.

- Polo befriended Chinese Emperor Kublai Khan, becoming one of his most valued diplomats. Polo was sent to various parts of the empire on official court business.

- Polo encountered the use of paper money while traveling in Asia—especially China—and introduced it to Italy where it caught on quickly.

- On his deathbed, he was encouraged to admit that his book was fiction, but he declared, "I did not tell half of what I saw."

Trade & Prosperity

As the Tuttle family prepared for dinner that evening, Mr. Tuttle laid out a special tablecloth that they used to study geography—a giant plastic map of the world. "Mom said you were talking about the Silk Road earlier. That sounds like a good dinner conversation to me," he said.

Mrs. Tuttle began bringing in the dishes of food and setting them on different sides of the table.

"Honey, you're in Western Europe." She put a plate of egg rolls on the English Channel, right in front of the spot where he usually sat.

Next she placed a bowl of steamed snow peas on the tallest mountains in the world. "Emily, you are in the Himalayas, in Tibet."

"Ethan, you're in the Mediterranean," Mrs. Tuttle said as she handed him some tongs.

Ethan looked a little confused. "But I wanted some food too."

"Don't worry," she replied. "We'll all get some after we trade, but not every job in trade involves making things... some people offer services. For example, ship crews and caravans carried products from marketplace to marketplace along the Silk Road."

"Because of this service, most people only had to travel as far as the nearest large city to sell their items to merchants, who would turn around and send them by ship or caravan to markets in other cities to resell them there. Marco Polo lived in northern Italy, and that's what his job was. So, Ethan... since you're sitting between Europe and the Middle East, you pretend to be our Mediterranean middleman—a merchant."

Ethan put his fist to the southeast of Mr. Tuttle, to claim Italy, the home country of Marco Polo.

Mr. Tuttle nodded. "Smart."

"And I'm in China," Mrs. Tuttle said, sitting down with a big bowl of the chicken lo mein that Ethan was now craving.

Then with a blue dry erase marker she traced a long line from Mr. Tuttle's egg rolls in Belgium, through France and Italy, across the Mediterranean sea to Turkey, Iran, the Himalayas, and all the way to China on the edge of the Pacific where she sat.

"There were alternate routes, even some by sea, but generally, that's the Silk Road," she said.

"That's a crazy long road," Ethan said, staring. "There are so many countries that it crosses."

"And there were even more countries, back in Marco Polo's day," Mrs. Tuttle added. "For a long time, it was the only way for Europeans to get spices and silk from China and wool and other cloth from Europe to China. As long as everyone traded fairly—or at least somewhat fairly—everyone got something, so all the different kingdoms allowed the road to stay open."

"Okay, can we bring *our* products to market now?" Mr. Tuttle suggested.

He, Mrs. Tuttle, and Emily pushed their food dishes along the silk road, closer to Ethan the merchant. Ethan put two egg rolls, some snow peas, and a mound of chicken lo mein onto plates for everyone, and passed them out.

"And for the service of making this trade possible at my Italian market, I shall take a plate for myself as payment," Ethan said.

"Done," Emily agreed. Everyone was happy.

"Italians also get dessert, right?" Ethan said.

Mr. Tuttle used chopsticks to shovel a bite of lo mein into his mouth with a big smile.

"You bet," he said. "As long as you also provide the service of doing the dishes."

"Deal," Ethan said. His stomach growled, and everyone laughed.

"See how that works?" Mr. Tuttle said. "We each traded something, and all of us ended up happier than we were when we started. Trade works that way. And that was why the Silk Road worked so well for more than a thousand years. When people are allowed to trade with each other, everyone's lives are improved."

"Too bad it didn't last," Mrs. Tuttle said.

"What happened? If everyone's lives were getting better, why would they end it?" Ethan said.

"The Mongol emperors of China ruled most of the lands along this route. They

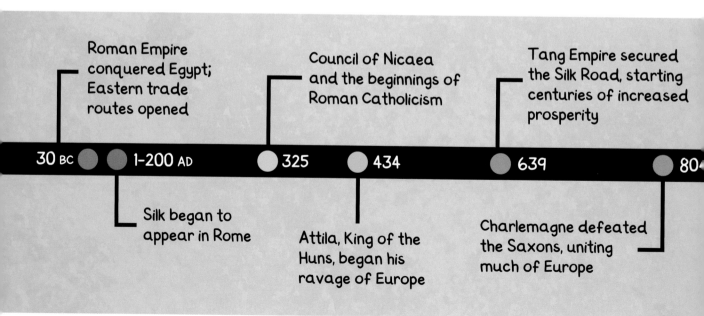

understood that keeping international trade flowing on the Silk Road brought them great wealth, so they used their military to protect caravans and merchants. But new kings rose up against Mongol rule, causing it to break up into smaller, warring nations. It became too chaotic and expensive to travel through these territories."

"Traders could still travel the sea routes through Egypt," Mr. Tuttle said, drawing another line in red. "But that way had its own problems."

"The Ottoman Empire developed a new technology for war—cannons!" he continued. "They took over the last stronghold of the Roman empire in Constantinople. This made trade more difficult, dangerous, and expensive through the Middle Eastern seaways, because the Ottomans wouldn't allow any traders through their lands without paying huge taxes."

Mr. Tuttle reached over and took the salt, pepper, and soy sauce off the table. "No more of this," he said. "Or these!" taking Ethan's dessert plate, too.

"Hey!" Ethan said. "I need that for my cake!"

"This," Mr. Tuttle said, "is porcelain. And it came from China, too."

Emily's eyes got wide. "Wait... that's why these plates and bowls and stuff are called 'China'?"

"Yes," Mr. Tuttle replied. "China plates were popular because they were easy to clean. So without them, Europeans had to use other types of dishes that were less sanitary. Also, without these spices,

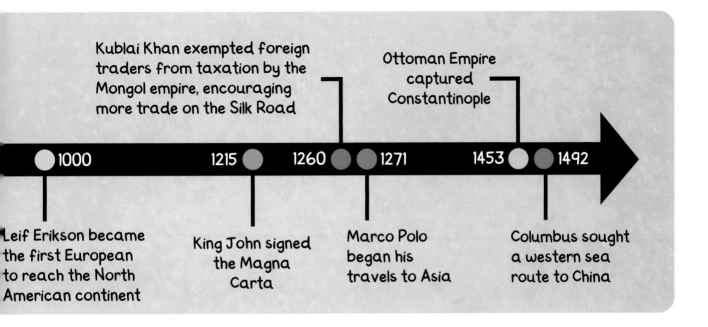

Kublai Khan exempted foreign traders from taxation by the Mongol empire, encouraging more trade on the Silk Road

Ottoman Empire captured Constantinople

1000   1215   1260   1271   1453   1492

Leif Erikson became the first European to reach the North American continent

King John signed the Magna Carta

Marco Polo began his travels to Asia

Columbus sought a western sea route to China

food got a lot more bland and spoiled faster. With trade cut off, life for everyone got much harder."

"Why didn't those governments just let everyone go back to trading?" Ethan asked. "Like how you're going to let me have my plate back so I can have a slice of cake…"

Mr. Tuttle put Ethan's plate back on the table. "Of course I will, because I trust you when you tell me you're going to do the dishes, so I'm happy to give you the cake now."

"Trust is what makes this whole system work. Actually, civilization is only possible when there's a certain amount of trust among the people. Would we have given our dishes of food to you if we believed you would have taken it all for yourself? Would Marco Polo have taken those long, dangerous journeys and paid for spices and silk if he didn't trust that he would be safe from Mongol hordes?"

"Nope. I would rather have had the entire bowl of snow peas, than nothing at all," Emily said.

"And if I treated you all unfairly, you wouldn't have let me be your merchant anymore," Ethan said.

"Exactly," Mr. Tuttle replied. "The Silk Road was an encouraging experiment. People of completely different cultures and religions—Romans, Egyptians, Mongols, and Arabs; Christians, Muslims, Hindus, and Buddhists—were able to interact, learn from each other, and benefit through trade. Compare that to the previous thousands of years of war against each other. They developed a certain level of trust and it had a great result."

"But that trust among all those different cultures was broken when the rulers of these empires began to go to war again. The other governments tried to keep the trade routes open, but it was too hard to do without everyone participating."

Mrs. Tuttle pointed at the map. "With the overland road closed, and the seaways through Egypt getting too dangerous and expensive, some Portuguese explorers were ready to try something new. They attempted to sail around Africa. If they succeeded, they could become rich like the Italian merchants who controlled the Mediterranean sea ports."

"That's a lot farther, though," Ethan said, drawing a new line on the map, from Portugal, down the coast of Africa, around the Cape of Good Hope and into the Indian Ocean. He continued his line on land through India, then to China. "But I guess it's possible."

"And dangerous," Mrs. Tuttle said. "They had to make their ships sail very fast to make it worth the risk, but still their navigation wasn't very good yet. If they lost sight of land, they'd have trouble knowing where they were. You see, Africa was a mysterious continent that Europeans hadn't mapped yet. No one had been that far South—at least no one that ever came back."

The twins' eyes widened. "People that never came back?" Ethan said, looking at Emily. "Maybe that means more bandits."

"Or pirates!" Emily added.

"Enough of this for now," Mr. Tuttle said, getting up and bringing a cake pan to the table. "Time for dessert. Emily, you get the first slice."

After the meal was over and the dishes were done, Ethan sat on his bed thinking, staring out the window. He wasn't really worried, but he couldn't stop thinking about the bandits and pirates—men who tried to stop people from trading. Really, they were stopping people from having better lives. And what kind of person did that? Good thing there weren't any people around like that anymore.

Or were there?

As he laid down, he noticed the tree in the backyard, where it bent in the breeze, throwing soft shadows over the side of the house. The moon loomed large, shining brightly. The same moon that once shone down on the Silk Road. The moon saw everything, all over the world. Ethan wanted to ask it all kinds of questions, but before he could, his eyes closed and he fell asleep.

A Western Passage?

The next morning, Ethan rubbed the sleep from his eyes and wandered into the kitchen. On the table stood a box of Loopy Fruits and a bowl. Mr. Tuttle must have gone to work early and left the cereal out.

Still thinking about what he'd learned the night before, Ethan began to pour some cereal. But he was tired and spilled some on the table. He went to sweep them back up, when he noticed that they'd run off in a line not too far from the blue line that his mother had drawn representing the Silk Road.

He imagined the pieces of cereal were a line of camels and people—a caravan crossing rivers, going over mountains, carrying sacks of products, and buying and selling from city to city. He arranged some pieces, pretending they were Italian ships sailing across the Mediterranean Sea to ports in Turkey and Egypt. Then

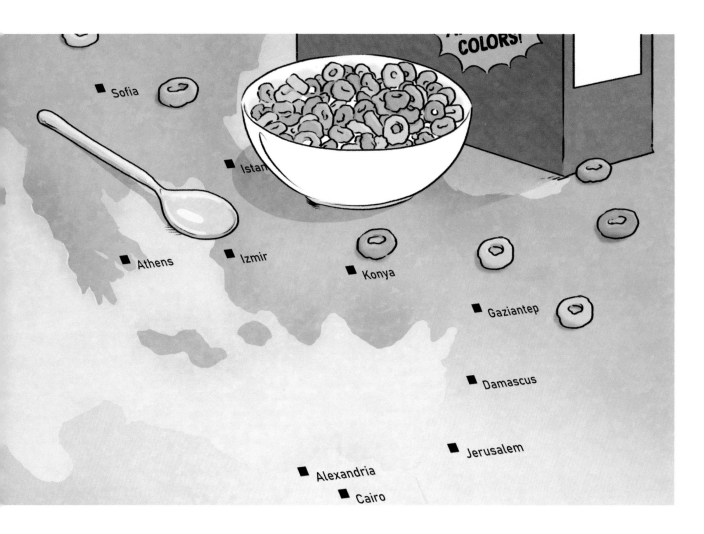

he arranged others for Arab and Indian ships on the Red Sea and Indian Ocean, and Portuguese ships sailing around the tip of Africa, the Cape of Good Hope.

Emily sat down across from Ethan at the table. He hadn't heard her come in.

She didn't say anything for a while. Then she reached out and picked up a piece of cereal from the Silk Road, uncovering Damascus. She popped it in her mouth.

"Hey!" Ethan said. "That was my camel."

"Sorry, Mr. Camel," she said, still crunching.

Emily considered the map for a moment. "I think having to travel all the way around Africa was only part of what made the Silk Road's closing so disappointing."

"What do you mean?"

"What did Mom say the caravans carried?"

"Silk. Jade. Spices. And apparently, porcelain dishes," Ethan said. "Or if they were coming from Europe, then cloth, wool, and wood."

"Right," Emily said. She pointed to Jerusalem. "Look, some of those things

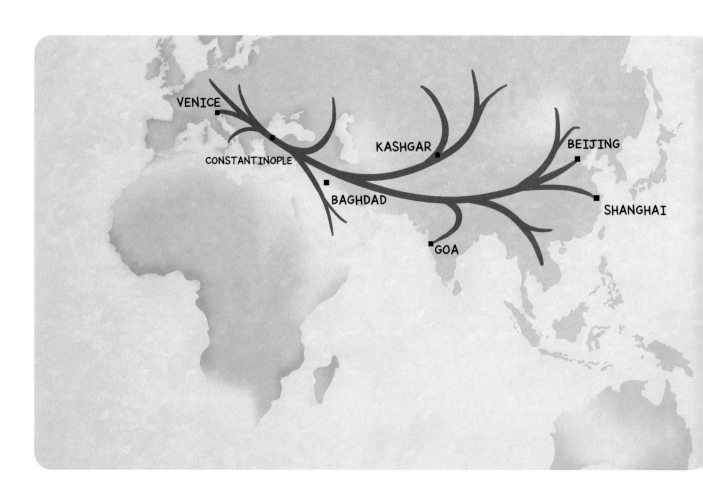

would be valuable right there too—not just in China or Italy. These people had other products to trade, like dates and figs and spices—"

"Spices like Frankenstein and murder?" Ethan smiled.

"Frankincense and myrrh!" Emily replied, rolling her eyes. "As you know very well."

Ethan laughed, but he saw what she was getting at. "So I bring wool from Italy, and I trade some of it for dates and *myrrh*, then take that to Damascus, where I trade that stuff for other things. What do they have in Damascus?"

Emily shrugged. "Steel? Didn't they make swords in Damascus?"

"Okay, steel, then. I take the steel to Kabul and get gold. I take the gold to China and get silk. Then I come back and do the same thing. All of the different marketplaces were adding their own local products."

He started adding more cereal to the map along the overland trade routes that connected all the different cities of Europe, the Middle East, and Asia. He imagined countless different products from a thousand different places all being traded on the Silk Road—a route that connected the world's people like vines

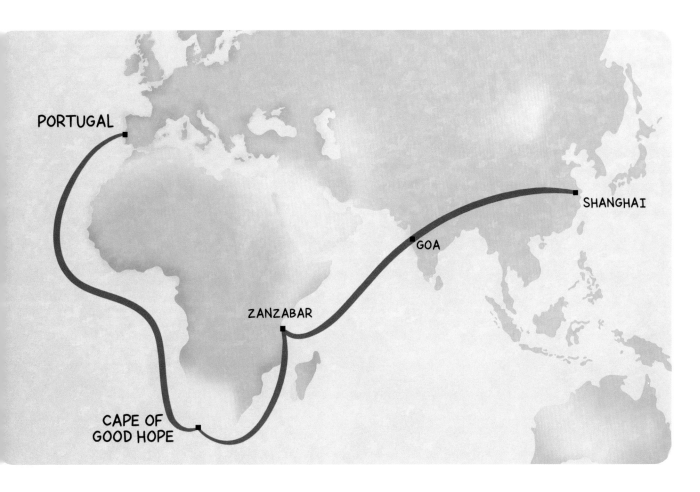

PORTUGAL

SHANGHAI

GOA

ZANZABAR

CAPE OF
GOOD HOPE

of ivy covering the exterior walls of the old church in town.

Emily reached out and swept up half the cereal pieces right from the middle of the line, tossing them into her mouth. "And then the Ottomans cut it all off," she said through her crunching sounds.

"I can still go by sea," Ethan said, but he could see how hard that would be. So much longer. Fewer major trading ports. Fewer products and people to trade with. It wouldn't work nearly as well—like a grocery store that was 100 miles away and only had a few expensive products instead of a thousand low-priced ones.

Mrs. Tuttle came through the room with arms full of laundry. She stopped and looked over the map. "Too bad that it took them so long," she finally said, "to try going the other way."

"What other way?" Ethan said, getting up to fetch a wayward sock that had fallen out of the basket.

"West," Mrs. Tuttle said. "West from Europe. Finding a trade route that didn't have to go quite so far." She nodded her head at the cereal ships sailing from Portugal around Africa to China. "This journey took them months."

"Uh, Mom," Emily said. "It's not shorter to go west. I'll show you."

"Yeah, there's a whole continent in the way," Ethan said, pointing at North America.

"Two continents," Emily said, pointing to South America.

"That would be a very long line," Ethan said. "Definitely not faster."

Mrs. Tuttle smiled. "Yes, you're both very smart. But the people in Europe were smart too, only they didn't have satellites to tell them there was a lot of land in the way. They had to run into it in order to learn about it the hard way. I bet you can name one explorer from history who was brave enough to try it."

"Christopher Columbus," Ethan said. "When he set sail he was looking for a new route to China, right?"

"That's right," Mrs. Tuttle said. "In all four of Columbus's expeditions to the New World, he thought he had sailed around the world and was exploring the coasts of Asia."

"So he never realized what he actually discovered? That's too bad," Emily remarked.

"But your next expedition needs to be to your room to fold these clothes. And while you're doing that, I'll make a call. I know just the right person to share what happened next."

A Thought From Connor

You might be wondering right now what any of this has to do with American history. To understand how our nation began, we have to understand the early events and circumstances that led people to explore the world.

Trade was improving so many people's lives, and this encouraged some people to venture further distances in hopes of finding new opportunities. As people became more prosperous through trade, they began to think differently about how their governments were sometimes getting in the way of their efforts to create a better life for themselves.

Let's Talk About It!

What if people along the Silk Road decided to stop their trading activities and instead focused on supporting their local industries? How might the world have changed because people prioritized buying from and selling to their neighbors instead of people from faraway lands?

It's fairly common to hear people in the United States of America advocate "Buy American!" This means they want to encourage (or require) people to trade with people in their country instead of people from other countries.

What are the downsides of this policy?

And what problems might start happening if the government interferes in our ability to trade freely? Sometimes governments will punish trade through taxes called *tariffs* or stop it altogether using *sanctions*.

What would the world look like if people could trade freely with one another?

Chapter 2

New Lands & New Ideas

A Mysterious Visitor

The next morning, Emily woke to a knock on the door. She lay in bed for a moment, wondering what time it was. Sunlight was just beginning to slant through the window and illuminate parts of the floor. The house was too quiet. There was no noise from the kitchen where Mom and Dad would be, and no thumping and bumping from Ethan's room. Did everyone else leave? Surely not.

The knock came again, but this time, the sound of footsteps led from the living room to the door. Light, quick steps. It was her mother.

The front door opened, and Emily heard a muffled conversation. She couldn't tell what was being said, but the voice at the door was low and deep. Mrs. Tuttle laughed. Then she called out, "Hey twins! Someone is here to see you."

Emily rolled over and threw on her fluffy robe and a pair of slippers. She got to the hallway just in time to see Ethan come out of his room, his hair like a rat's nest.

"Did Mom really call us to the door? It's not even seven o'clock yet," he said.

"Yes, she did. It sounds like a man."

"What man wants to talk to us... and this early?"

Emily put her arm around her brother as they started down the staircase—she was afraid he might fall over if she didn't. "We might as well find out."

Mom stood to one side, revealing a man framed in the doorway. It was their good friend Fred from next door. He was dressed funny, though. He wore a dark cape and shirt, with a big white collar, a tall hat with a brass buckle, and pants that stopped just below the knee. Below that, tall black stockings and glossy black shoes completed the costume.

"Hail, Master Ethan!" he called out. "And to you, Mistress Emily. Fine day, is it not?"

Emily felt curiously shy. Why was he talking like that—so formal and old-fashioned? "Very fine, sir," she said, trying to speak like him. "And may I wish you good health?"

"Of course you may. What excellent manners! You should be very proud, Goodwife Tuttle," he said to Mrs. Tuttle.

"I am, of course. But you said that you had a message for the kids?"

"Indeed, forgive me," Fred said. He held out two folded slips of paper. "For you, Mistress Emily. And one for you, Master Ethan."

The twins took the papers. They were yellowed, as if very old, and they were sealed shut with a dollop of red wax pressed down with a stamp that had a fancy letter "F".

Emily didn't want to open hers because it might break the pretty seal. Fred saw the worry in her face. "You might use a sharp knife," he suggested, "and slide it under the seal. That should do it."

Emily wanted to run into the kitchen for a knife right away, but she knew it would be poor manners to leave the room just yet. So she dropped one leg behind the other and dipped into a curtsey. "Many thanks, good sir. Would you care to take breakfast with us?"

He bowed back to her, with a bright smile on his face. "No, mistress. But thank you for the fine offer. I believe we will see one another soon." He bowed to Ethan. "Master Ethan." Then to Mrs. Tuttle. "Goodwife Tuttle."

"Bye, Goodman Fred," Mrs. Tuttle said, and closed the door as he turned to go.

"What on earth?" Ethan said. "What is all this 'Goodman' and 'Goodwife' stuff? And what am I supposed to be a master of?"

"Or me, a mistress?" Emily said.

Mrs. Tuttle just smiled and led the way into the kitchen where she fetched the sharp paring knife and handed it to Emily. Emily carefully slid the blade under the seal, lifting it from the paper, and started to read. "To Mistress Tuttle, a formal invitation requesting your presence for a story adventure in American history. This afternoon, at 3pm sharp. Refreshments provided!"

"Alright, refreshments!" Ethan said. He didn't bother using the knife and ripped the letter open. His said the same as Emily's did. "That means snacks."

"And a story," Emily said. "Maybe we can ask questions about the Silk Road and Columbus."

"Fred, er, I mean *Goodman* Fred knows everything," Ethan replied. "He'll have answers for sure. We'll have time for talking *and* eating. Nice."

To Mistress Tuttle,
A formal invitation requesting – your presence for a story – adventure in American history This afternoon, at 3pm sharp.
Refreshments provided!
- Fred

The Age of Exploration

They knocked promptly at 3:00, Emily swishing her dress back and forth and Ethan tugging uncomfortably on his tie. They heard footsteps, and the door opened. Fred stood there in the same outfit that he wore that morning.

"Come in! Come in!" Fred said. He swept his arm in invitation.

Emily was glad she'd taken her mother's advice to wear a dress. Fred was so dressed up that she would have felt a little funny in her regular clothes. She and Ethan came in and Fred closed the door behind them. The twins felt a bit awkward, but thankfully Fred was all fun and welcoming.

"We'll be having our conversation in my study today," Fred said, moving past them toward the stairs. The twins knew this room well—it was a special place for them. They had sat there learning important lessons from Fred before. Bookshelves packed with books, maps, and artwork covered the walls from floor to ceiling. Emily saw some familiar titles, but there were several books laid out on the table that she didn't know—*Pilgrim's Progress*, *Confessions*, *On the Social Contract*, and *Discourses on Livy*.

Fred patted the old leather couch and asked them to sit, then he settled himself into a wide burgundy chair with brass tacks on the arms. To his left, a small table was piled high with more old books, and to his right, a fold-out tray bore what looked like flat brown cookies.

"Thank you for coming to see me," he said. "Your mother tells me you're interested in the Age of Exploration."

Ethan's face was blank. "I don't think I know what that is."

Fred laughed. "The Age of Exploration is a period during the Renaissance."

"We learned about Leonardo da Vinci and the Renaissance on our trip to Italy," Emily said excitedly. "He was a great artist and inventor."

"That's right! He and many others of his time were fascinated with learning and thinking about things in new ways. They studied art, music, math, biology, chemistry, and astronomy. They discussed new ideas about philosophy, religion, politics, and economics. They were also fascinated with learning about the earth and the exploration of it. It was an exciting time."

"We talked with Mom about Christopher Columbus yesterday. He wanted to get to China by traveling westward around the earth," Ethan said.

"Did you know that da Vinci and Christopher Columbus may have known one another? They were both from northern Italy, almost the same age, and well-known Renaissance men."

"Wow! I didn't realize they lived at the same time," Emily said.

Fred reached down between his chair and the table of books and procured a small, framed map. "This is a map of the exploration of the world from 1500 to 1600—the Age of Exploration. Right after Columbus's expedition, everyone became even more fanatical about adventure and exploration of the world. It was probably the greatest period of exploration in human history, even though they still only learned a tiny fraction of what there was to know."

"I bet they were also interested in learning about new trade routes," Ethan said. "Our dad explained how the trade routes of the Silk Road were like branches of a vine spreading useful products all over Europe and Asia. They helped everyone have a better life. So after the Silk Road was blocked, people's lives got worse and they wanted to find another way."

"Marco Polo, another Italian," Fred said, picking up one of the books that was beside him titled *Book of the Marvels of the World*.

"So that's the book he wrote, huh?" Emily said.

"Christopher Columbus read Marco Polo's book about his adventures on the Silk Road. That's what got him excited about exploration," Fred said. "And I'm sure you know about Columbus opening the way to the New World."

Ethan nodded. "Yes, we learned about that, too. But... why did so many important people come from Italy?"

"Excellent question, Ethan!" Fred said. He seemed so excited by the question that he almost had to catch his breath before continuing. "You see, most of the world lived under the reign of some king, lord, or emperor. The Roman Empire, the Persian Empire, the Mongol Empire, the Ottoman Empire... these governments used war to conquer other lands and enslave the people to make themselves rich. This way of ruling is called *feudalism*."

The looks on the twins' faces showed they thought feudalism sounded awful. "It almost sounds like a bad word," remarked Emily.

Fred chuckled, then continued. "The small republics of Italy were in a unique situation. The capital of the Roman Empire had moved to Constantinople, so this gave local merchants more control in making laws for their own cities. Instead of building armies for conquest, they built fleets of ships for the adventure of travel and business. For hundreds of years, they were largely left alone to freely trade without being controlled and taxed so much. Does that make sense?"

"I think so. With feudalism, the peasants had to be slaves for the king, or else!" Emily said. "But you're saying that in Italy, people were able to work for themselves."

"Also, as you know, Italy is on the Mediterranean Sea with many shipping ports. It was also on the edge of the Silk Road," Fred continued. "So it became a major center of shipping, banking, and trade—making its people very rich and exposing the locals to a lot of ideas and innovations."

"Like the Polo family!" Ethan said.

"Yes, and the influential Medici family as well," Fred added.

"I bet the Italians were really upset when the Ottoman Empire took over Constantinople and blocked the Silk Road," Emily thought out loud. "Bad for business."

"Yeah, they used their new cannon technology to blast down the city walls!" Ethan said. "Boom! Boom! Boom!"

More About Us!

Bartolomeu Dias
1450 – 1500

Earning glory for his country of Portugal, Dias demonstrated the most effective southern route to Asia when he became the first European to round the tip of Africa in 1488. It was because of this triumph that most of the royal sponsors were less interested in Columbus's idea of traveling around the earth.

Christopher Columbus
1451 – 1506

Columbus spent years asking Europe's royalty to fund an Atlantic voyage, seeking a western route to the Orient. Finally in 1492, the King and Queen of Spain agreed. His four voyages were successful, opening a period of exploration, conquest, and colonization that lasted for several centuries.

Amerigo Vespucci
1451 – 1512

Vespucci made two voyages to the New World on behalf of Spain (1499) and Portugal (1501). He realized during these expeditions that what they were exploring wasn't the coast of Asia, but a new continent entirely. Because of this, map makers later deemed the new land "America" in honor of his work.

Sebastian Cabot
1474 – 1557

Inspired by the exploration of his father years earlier, Sebastian made the first detailed accounts of the North American coast in 1508, theorizing that the Hudson River was a passage through the continent to China. He claimed the land for the King, but Henry VIII was not that interested in his explorations.

Ferdinand Magellan
1480 – 1521

Magellan's crew was the first to circumnavigate the earth from 1519-1522. Their expedition, around the tip of South America to the Spice Islands of Indonesia, was successful, but came at great cost. Magellan was killed in a battle in the Philippines in 1521. Of the five ships and 270-man crew that started the voyage, only 18 men and one ship survived the journey back to Spain.

Francis Drake
1540 – 1596

In 1577, this Englishman journeyed around South America to explore the western shores of the New World and to interfere with Spain's dominance on the continent. In his oversized and heavily armed galleon named *Golden Hind*, he raided many Spanish ships in port settlements for their gold. By completing his voyage traveling westward, he became the second explorer to circumnavigate the earth.

"You know about that, huh? Well that battle is actually an important event that sparked the age of the Renaissance," Fred said. "Romans who escaped from Constantinople brought back to Italy the traditions and culture of old Greece and Rome—which of course used to be the capital city of the Roman Empire. The Northern Italians, in Venice especially, had a renewed interest in the old ways of classical philosophy, art, architecture, music, and science. That's actually what renaissance means: rebirth."

"It's really interesting how all of these things are connected together," Emily remarked. "One thing starts another, like a chain reaction."

"Exactly, but it's a chain reaction that multiplies in different directions, like branches of the vine your dad mentioned," Fred said. "For example, the Ottomans taking Constantinople didn't just cause the Renaissance in Italy; it also closed the Silk Road, which caused the sea routes to be used more, which made the Portuguese look for a new route around Africa."

"And why were the Portuguese, and the Spanish as well, so interested in finding new trade routes?" Fred asked the twins. "Put simply, they were pretty jealous of the Italians' wealth from trade. But the Spanish were especially desperate, and that's why they took the risk to pay for

Columbus's journey around the world when no one else would."

"Seems like the Age of Exploration was just another branch of the vine, growing out of things that happened before, on and on back through history," Emily said quietly, thinking of how connected everything was.

"Kind of makes my head hurt trying to think about it all," Ethan agreed.

"If you think the results of the Battle of Constantinople hurt your head, just wait," Fred chuckled. "The next thing I'm going to talk to you about affected everyone, everywhere, forever."

Emily blinked slowly, wondering what the next branch of the vine might be.

"But I can tell we need to take a short break before both of your minds burst with knowledge!"

Ethan let out a happy little sigh as Fred presented a porcelain plate of cookies. They were crispy and delicious— gingerbread with just a hint of cinnamon. He shook his head, laughing softly at the realization. Spices. A plate from China. Products that used to be traded along the Silk Road. The twins would never think about those simple things in the same way again.

The Power of Knowledge

The three sat quietly eating cookies and sipping cold milk, enjoying the afternoon sun that was now beaming through the window, illuminating many of the titles on the spines of the books on the shelves. Ethan began to relax.

Two days ago, they had been playing Marco Polo in the swimming pool, not imagining that it would lead to them learning so much history. Even though Ethan's brain was tired from the intense mental workout, he was really enjoying it—but he was curious how all these events from the past were connected to American history, which is what Fred's invitation was about.

"Some people say I have too many books," Fred said, breaking the silence. "But all these books remind me every day not to take my wonderful life for granted. Ethan and Emily, you and I have comfort, peace, and freedom like no one ever imagined possible. We are free from feudalism... because of books."

"Books?" Emily asked.

"Yes, books," Fred replied. "Just like trade routes spread products to all the people of the world, the availability of books spread knowledge and new ideas, thanks to the invention of the printing press. Ethan, you were transporting products on your trade route, weren't you? Silks and tea and wool?"

"And pepper and jade and things like that. That's right," Ethan said, sitting forward.

"Those things are important, certainly. Trade brought about the Age of Exploration. But books brought the exploration of *ideas*. This changed the world far more drastically than those products—more than anyone could have ever imagined. Look at all the books in this library," Fred said, sweeping his arm in a circle. "Every one of them is filled with ideas from people from all over the world. If we didn't have books, how would those ideas have spread and not be lost to history?"

"I'm guessing the Internet wouldn't have been a possibility back then," Emily said, as Ethan rolled his eyes.

"No, definitely not," Fred smiled. "In fact, without books there wouldn't be an Internet today. There wouldn't be cars, phones, or most of the technologies we enjoy. There wouldn't even be a United States of America."

"What?!" Ethan said. "How could books make a country exist?"

"I'm glad you asked. That's exactly the reason I asked you to come over today,

- Johannes Gutenberg was exiled from his hometown when the local craftsmen revolted against him and other noble families. He moved to Strasbourg where he invented the movable type printing press.

- He adapted a wine press to build his first machine. Instead of pressing grapes, the equipment pressed metal letter forms onto sheets of paper.

- The first printing press made it to America in 1639. It was run out of Cambridge, Massachusetts. The use of the printing press was vital to spreading the ideas of freedom in the colonies. One of the most successful printed books was Thomas Paine's *Common Sense*!

and the reason I'm dressed up like this," Fred said, reaching for the next book from the stack on the table. "The printing press was even more revolutionary than computers."

Emily took the book Fred was holding and turned it over in her hands. The leather of the cover, the stitching of the binding, even the slightly raised print on the page—all of it felt so natural in her hands. She loved the feel of it. Reading books was enjoyable for her, certainly, but she had not thought a lot about how books were made and when they were invented.

"Johannes Gutenberg—that's who invented the press that allowed that book to be printed," he said.

"In Europe, most of the governments were monarchies, remember? Kings and queens wielded great power over people, but the Pope of the Roman Catholic Church had power over what people believed, which at the time was an even greater power than all the monarchs of Europe. And people only knew what someone told them, since most people couldn't read—but that hardly mattered because there wasn't anything to read, anyway."

"Feudalism," Emily said. "And no books."

"There was one very important book," Fred said, "but there were very few copies because each copy had to be written by hand in Latin, a language few people spoke anymore. He reached out and tapped the old book Emily was holding. "The book was called—"

"The Bible, of course," Ethan said matter-of-factly.

"That's right. But because few people could read it for themselves, they had to believe whatever their rulers told them to believe, and no one could argue with them. Both their bodies and their minds were enslaved. But after a while, some heroic people decided to make it so everyone could read the Bible in the language they spoke. Peter Waldo, John Wycliffe, and many others translated the Bible into the everyday languages of the people. Many of them were killed for it."

Ethan was shocked. "Killed for helping others read the Bible?"

"What's so wrong about people knowing what was in the Bible?" Emily asked. "Why would they be threatened by people learning about their own religion?"

"Here's a big question for you," Fred said in reply, looking each of the twins in the eye. "It's an important question that philosophers have been thinking about for thousands of years... and now I want you to try to answer it." He sat back in his chair and put one leg over the other, preparing to say something important.

"What makes something right or wrong? Who decides?"

Ethan thought for a moment, realizing that the answer might be a little more complicated than what first came to his mind. "It's wrong to steal, and lie, and it's wrong to hurt people. That's what we were taught by our mom and dad since we were toddlers."

"And their parents taught them the same thing? So where did it start?" Fred asked.

"Well... if we did those things we'd go to jail. There are laws about stealing and murder," Emily said.

"Then is it the government? Those ancient kings and rulers invented right and wrong?" Fred asked. He cocked an eyebrow, knowing Emily didn't really believe that.

"That definitely can't be true, because governments throughout history have done awful things and made very bad laws," Ethan said. "So right and wrong isn't just because a king made a law."

Fred gently took the old Bible from Emily. "This book, the Gutenberg Bible, was printed in German. Fortunately, I know some passages by heart."

"Exodus, chapter 20: 'Thou shalt have no other gods before me.' Acts, chapter 5: 'We should obey God rather than men.' Matthew, chapter 6: 'No one can serve two masters.' These are just a few of many passages that carried a powerful

idea—that right and wrong came from a law higher than any man, king, or priest." Fred paused to see if the concept was clear to the twins.

"So that's why the kings and the popes didn't want the people to understand the Bible on their own," Ethan said, working it out in his mind. "If the people started believing that their rulers were doing bad things, then the rulers might lose control over them."

"And that's what began to happen. You've probably heard of Martin Luther, a Roman Catholic priest who challenged the teachings of his church," Fred said. "Others who agreed with him started what was known as the Protestant Reformation. One church soon grew into hundreds, including one that is particularly important to our story, the Church of England—the Anglican Church. You see, King Henry didn't want to be controlled by the Pope anymore— he wanted all the power to make the rules. So poof, a new church was born." Fred snapped his fingers.

Fred put the Gutenberg Bible down on the table and picked up another from the stack. "This Bible is called the Geneva Bible. This is a very significant version of the Bible, printed in English. It was used by another Protestant group called the Puritans."

"But if the Roman Catholic church and the kings had all that power, wouldn't they try to stop the people?" Ethan asked.

"Well, yes, they tried," Fred replied. "Remember, these rulers *did* kill some of the rebellious preachers, but it was too late. Thousands of people who had read these ideas now questioned the authority of their rulers and rejected the idea that they could tell them how to live and what to believe. It became impossible to keep all the people from reading and expressing their opinions."

"And as you'll come to learn," Fred added, "this access to information—the power to print a book—led to the creation of this country we're in."

"So the printing press helped create the United States of America!" Ethan said.

"Yes, precisely," Fred chuckled. "Only, not yet—remember there isn't a U.S.A. at this point. And there are hardly even any settlers, just Spanish and Portuguese explorers looking for gold and silver. But back in Europe, these rebellious ideas were creating an incentive for people to find a new place to freely practice religion in their own way."

"It's amazing the changes the printing press caused," Ethan said as he reached for another cookie, astonished at the impact one invention could have on so many people.

Fred grabbed a cookie as well. "One Protestant, John Knox, argued right to the queen's face that she was only the queen because the people allowed it. Can you imagine the courage he had?"

"I bet the queen didn't like that very much," Ethan said. "It's got to be a little hard when you're used to clapping your hands, and people jump up and go. Now you have to make sense and be good to them; otherwise, they might rebel."

"Yeah, how awful..." Emily said sarcastically. "Now that people can read the Bible, you have to start acting like you actually believe it!" She shook her head.

Everyone got a laugh out of that. Fred glanced at his watch.

"Hey," Emily said. "You've got a watch on. That's not something they would have had in the old days, is it?"

Fred looked surprised, a little smile on his face. "You caught me. In fact, most people didn't even care what time it was until years later. But I have an appointment that I need to get to in just a bit, so I indulged myself."

More About Us!

Martin Luther
1483 – 1546

Henry VIII
1491 – 1547

John Calvin
1509 – 1564

Once a Catholic priest, he was excommunicated and made an outlaw after he posted a list of doctrinal disagreements on the door of the All Saints' Church in Germany. He continued preaching his understanding of religious principles. After some time, his followers began calling themselves Lutherans.

This was the beginning of the Protestant Reformation; Protestants were Christians who did not follow the teachings and authority of the Roman Catholic Church.

In his time, divorce was forbidden by the Catholic Church. Taking matters into his own hands, he organized and led the Anglican Church (the Church of England). With that privilege and power, he was married six times!

This new church was technically Protestant, but many in England felt it was far too similar to Catholicism. This would eventually inspire the Puritan movement, which sought to cleanse the Church of England of its Catholic traditions.

Raised as a Roman Catholic, Calvin encountered the ideas of Martin Luther while attending school. In 1536, he began publishing his views called *Institutes of the Christian Religion*; these views helped systematize Protestant activity throughout Europe.

His reformed theology inspired others like John Knox, who founded the Presbyterian Church of Scotland and the Puritan movement in England.

"What's that costume, anyway?" Ethan said. "It looks like the drawings of Hans Brinker in one of my books. Is it Dutch?"

"Very close," Fred said, taking off his hat and handing it over for the twins to look at. "Many of the people who dressed like this *did* live in Holland, though most weren't Dutch. They came from England—they fled England because King James (who ruled a century after Henry) said everyone had to be part of the Anglican Church and believe its teachings. But this faithful group wanted to worship in their own way, so they had to flee or lose their lives."

"King James? We have a Bible at home called the King James Bible," Emily said. She stroked the gold buckle that held the strap onto the black velvet hat. It was smooth and shone in the sunlight. "I guess that was another version of the Bible he printed for his Anglican church?"

"Correct, Emily," he replied. "The power of the English Monarchy was being threatened by Catholics and other Protestant groups who didn't like the Anglican Church. Part of the reason King James and his priests made that Bible was to keep people from questioning his authority. If he controlled what they believed, he could also control their behavior. Sadly, many wars were fought in order to stop people from worshiping in different ways that they preferred."

"That sounds so crazy," she said. "We have lots of friends who practice different religions. I can't imagine fighting a war over people's beliefs."

Fred nodded. "Fortunately, there were a few places people could go to find religious freedom. For one group of Puritan refugees, they found Holland to be a safe place for a while. Eventually, though, they weren't happy there, either. But they heard about someplace even better."

"The New World," Ethan said enthusiastically. "I knew I'd seen this costume before. The Pilgrims, right?"

"From Plymouth Rock!" Emily said.

"You're both very bright, you know that?" Fred said. "This is—as best we know—the clothing of the Puritan Pilgrims of Plymouth, who were among the first settlers of New England."

Fred reached to the table and slid open the drawer. He reached in and took out two yellowed pieces of paper, like the ones the twins' invitations had been written on. He handed one to Ethan and the other to Emily. The papers were covered in swooping black letters. They were hard to read, but Ethan thought he could make out the words "name of God" and "Amen" on it.

"You may take these with you," Fred said, standing up. "It's a document you should know and have a copy of. It's called the Mayflower Compact."

"The Mayflower," Emily said with recognition in her voice. She gently took the parchment. After what they had learned that day—about the power of the printed word—it felt like she was holding something very special.

"These are just replicas, of course. Fred started to grin. "I'm not *that* old. But it's a decent copy. Take it with you, and when you come back tomorrow, we'll talk about how this little document helped change the world."

"Prepare yourself to learn how a vine branch, started by the Pilgrims, grew all over the earth."

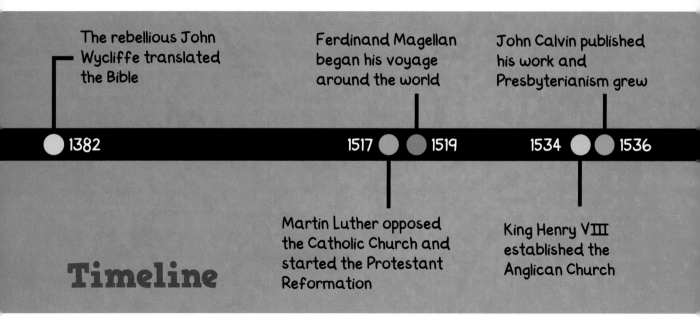

The rebellious John Wycliffe translated the Bible

Ferdinand Magellan began his voyage around the world

John Calvin published his work and Presbyterianism grew

Timeline

1382

1517 1519

1534 1536

Martin Luther opposed the Catholic Church and started the Protestant Reformation

King Henry VIII established the Anglican Church

A Thought From Elijah

A common theme you'll see throughout history is that seemingly small discoveries, or new ideas, can have huge results! All of our actions and words can create ripples of influence that might eventually change the world.

So what should you do with the realization that even *you* have such great power? First, I hope that you will be careful about what you say, write, and do that might hurt others. Our words and actions have real power, so we should be cautious about how we use them.

Secondly, I hope that you will be courageous and know that you really can make the world a better place. For example, think about how courageous Columbus and his crew must have been to travel out into the open sea, not knowing what they might find, if anything at all—or think of Martin Luther standing up to the entire Holy Roman Empire, or John Knox to the queen.

When people in the future look back at your life, what will they say about you? What will you do in your life, using the power of ideas and words, to make our world a better place for others?

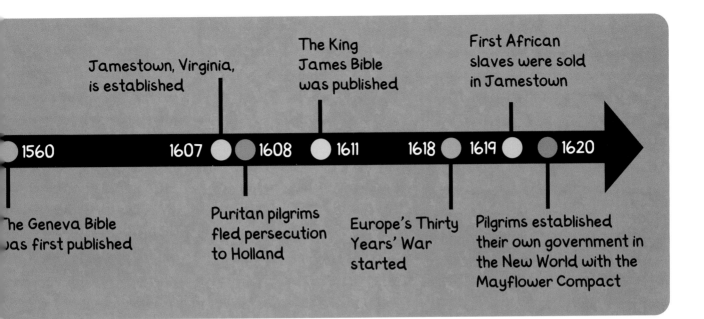

| 1560 | 1607 | 1608 | 1611 | 1618 | 1619 | 1620 |

Jamestown, Virginia, is established — 1607

The King James Bible was published — 1611

First African slaves were sold in Jamestown — 1619

The Geneva Bible was first published — 1560

Puritan pilgrims fled persecution to Holland — 1608

Europe's Thirty Years' War started — 1618

Pilgrims established their own government in the New World with the Mayflower Compact — 1620

Let's Talk About It!

It's important to be able to defend your beliefs, because our beliefs form our perception of reality. They affect how we make decisions and relate to others. Really, our beliefs are the foundation of our lives, so it's good to be cautious and logical before replacing them with other beliefs! We certainly shouldn't discard our beliefs just because they are unpopular, others make fun of them, or because they are not shared by the majority.

When our beliefs are challenged by new information or new ideas, it can sometimes make us feel uncomfortable. After all, no one wants to discover that they've been wrong! These emotions might tempt us to reject the new information—even if it's correct or good.

So, here's a question for you to discuss: How can we determine if we should change our beliefs when we are presented with new information or ideas?

Chapter 3
Far Across the Sea

The First Colonial Voyages

The twins rolled up on their bikes into a parking lot, and there was Fred, standing by the old church. Today, he was dressed a lot differently than the last time they saw him—in shorts, a sun hat, and a collared shirt, with a small backpack and a walking stick that looked like something from *The Hobbit*. Ethan and Emily wore hats, shorts, and T-shirts too, with hiking boots. Each had a water bottle hooked to a belt loop. Fred's backpack had a long tube that came up over his shoulder, and the twins guessed his backpack doubled as his water supply.

"Where are your fancy Pilgrim clothes?" Ethan asked, a little disappointed.

"Not appropriate for a hike, I'm afraid," Fred said, a big smile creasing his face. "But I have no doubt you'll see me in funny costumes many more times. For now, I thought it best to be comfortable."

They didn't have long to think this over, because Fred abruptly turned and threaded his way between some cars and across the parking lot toward a grassy area surrounded by trees—a little park where they sometimes played baseball. Emily shrugged toward Ethan, and she knew he was thinking the same thing she was: with Fred, nothing ever went quite how you expected.

Fred was walking so quickly that the twins almost had to sprint to catch up. The grass waved in the breeze—it hadn't been cut in a while, and came well up to their ankles.

"Our lesson today needs a little space," Fred said. "The world is a very big place, and we need to get some perspective on that. First, though, let's follow this trail."

They knew where the trail went; they'd hiked it once for a charity walk-a-thon that Mrs. Tuttle arranged last year. It was a big loop down along the river, and back up a gentle hill to the other side of the church.

Bright morning sunshine trickled through the trees, and sunbeams chased each other on the brown dirt of the path that thousands of feet had packed hard and smooth over the years. Ethan stepped on a scrubby weed and caught the sharp scent of peppermint. Fred didn't hurry, but his pace was steady, and the twins needed to keep their strides long to keep up with him.

They'd been walking for only five minutes when Fred got a little ahead of them and then disappeared. One moment he was there, and the next he'd vanished around a slight bend in the path. The twins jogged up to the bend, rounded a giant oak, and saw nothing at all but the dappled sunlight on an empty path.

"Where did he go?" Emily asked, looking all around them.

"I don't know," Ethan said, taking a few steps forward and trying to peer through the thick undergrowth. "He was just ahead of us, but now—"

"And I'm still ahead of you," Fred's voice came from the thicket to the right. "You just don't know where to look."

"Now I know, but I still can't see you," Ethan said. Nothing showed in the brush but waving branches and tiny leaves.

Emily bent down and pointed. "Right here," she said. "There's a hole in the hedge."

Fred's hands and walking stick appeared through the leaves and parted the bushes—standing there like Moses by the Red Sea, a wry smile on his face. "Well done, Emily. Come on now, no time for dawdling."

The twins scrambled through the gap Fred made, and found themselves on a much narrower path, but this one hadn't been used for years, it seemed.

"I never knew this was here," Emily said.

"Neither did I," added Ethan as he jumped a root in the path. "I thought I knew these woods."

In just a few minutes, Fred's bright red backpack had led them zig-zagging up a hill, and there, before them, was a view they'd have remembered for certain if they'd ever seen it before.

The path cut sharply to the right and continued along the top of the hill, but the ground in front of them sloped sharply away, almost like a cliff, so there was nothing between them and the panorama. What a view!

Below, at the bottom of the slope, miles of forest spread out in every direction, before giving out to a distant wide meadow exactly ahead of them. The whole landscape was sliced in half, by a mighty river.

"Wow!" Emily said.

"Wow is right," Fred said. "Only some of us old-timers know about this viewpoint, and we keep it a secret. So you two can come here, but no parties, okay?"

The twins nodded. Fred squinted and pointed toward the middle of the scene at a small stone building sitting at the edge of the river. "See that? How far away do you think that is?"

The blanket of trees made it difficult to guess. "A mile?" Emily said. "Maybe two?"

"A little further," Ethan said. "It's got to be more than two."

"Ethan is close. It's almost three miles from here to that old pump house. So what's the farthest thing you can see?"

Off in the far distance, well beyond the trees and meadows, a line of low hills ran from east to west, but the river had cut them in half with eons of erosion. Wedged in that gap was a bridge that connected their town, Spoonerville, to Malantown across the river. They all knew

there must be cars crossing, but it was too far to make them out. "The hills and that bridge," Emily answered. "I can't see any further than those."

Fred nodded. He reached in his pocket and pulled something out. "Hold out your hands," he said.

Into Emily's palm, and then Ethan's, Fred dropped some grains of rice, two for Emily and three for Ethan. The grains lay there in their hands, small and white like bugs.

"What's this?" Ethan said.

Fred held out his own hand in which was a single grain. "These are ships. Mine is called *New Netherland*. Yours, Emily, are the *Speedwell* and the *Mayflower*; yours, Ethan, are the *Susan Constant*, the *Godspeed*, and the *Discovery*. Not very big, are they?"

They weren't. In fact, they were so small that the least breeze might have blown them from their hands and into the underbrush.

"I thought ships were bigger," Ethan joked.

"Very keen observation," Fred said, chuckling. "But the ocean is a lot bigger, too. Those hills, far off, are the foothills of the Arramack Mountains. There's another

Susan Constant
Virginia Co. of London
Jamestown – May 13, 1607

Godspeed
Virginia Co. of London
Jamestown – May 13, 1607

Discovery
Virginia Co. of London
Jamestown – May 13, 1607

park by that bridge about six miles away. That's where your parents will be picking us up. It will take us three hours to get there. Before we get going, let's pretend that we're standing on the shores of Europe. If those hills are the coasts of North America, the mighty *Mayflower*—or any of these ships—would be a grain of rice, to scale."

"So small," Emily breathed as she imagined a hundred tiny Pilgrims standing on her ships—the delicate grains of rice.

"That's quite the distance," Ethan said. "And the ocean is so big, and deep, and dangerous." Just then, a warm breeze rustled through the valley of trees, and for a brief moment it really felt and sounded like they were standing on the shores of the Atlantic Ocean.

"How it must have felt to be those first passengers. Families—women and children—about to cross into the unknown, never to return," Fred said. "Emily, your two ships represent the

Plymouth Company. That's what the business was called that sponsored the voyage. They tried to come with two ships, the *Speedwell* and the *Mayflower*."

"Ethan, your ships were sponsored by the London Company, and mine are from the Dutch East India Company. You two are trying to get to—"

"I know!" Emily said. "Massachusetts."

Fred smiled, but shook his head. "Actually, no. But I'll explain. Both the Plymouth and London Company wanted to put colonies in Virginia. Only... things didn't go according to plan for Emily's ships. My ship from Holland is headed to New York, or as they would have called it back then, New Amsterdam. So our journey begins!"

Fred abruptly shot off again through some thick brush, but in a few seconds the three of them were walking together again down the path. Not the path that Ethan and Emily knew from their mom's walk-a-thon, but down this new path they'd never known existed. A real adventure!

Speedwell
Virginia Co. of Plymouth
Failed voyage – 1620

Mayflower
Virginia Co. of Plymouth
Cape Cod – Nov. 21, 1620

New Netherlands
Dutch West India Company
Hudson River Valley – May 1624

After several minutes, Fred stopped dead in his tracks. "Oops," he said. "Looks like there's a problem with one of your ships, Emily. The *Speedwell* sprung a leak. You'll have to go back and leave her behind."

Emily glanced around. "You mean back to the viewpoint?"

"Yes," Fred said. "That's our point of departure. It's okay. We'll wait."

Emily's eyes and mouth opened so wide in disbelief that Ethan couldn't help but giggle. But also he felt sorry that Fred was requiring his sister to backtrack, even if it was just a football field's distance back.

"Wait. What about all the passengers of the *Speedwell*?" Emily asked. "They won't all fit onto the *Mayflower*, will they?"

"No, they won't. The two ships were already pretty packed when they set off, but they hadn't gone far when the *Speedwell* began to not speed so well."

Ethan giggled again. He loved corny jokes.

Fred continued, "The Speed-not-so-well was beginning to sink so both ships, full of Pilgrims, turned back, took everything and everyone off the *Speedwell*, and packed as many as they could into the *Mayflower*. So Emily, I'm sorry but you have to run that grain of rice back to the viewpoint."

Emily hustled off and returned several minutes later, a bit out of breath with only one grain in her hand. "Okay, now can we go to Virginia? How much longer?"

"Remember how big the ocean is?" Fred replied. "This trip is going to take seventy days."

"That's a very long time to be on a boat," Ethan said. "I hope our hike doesn't go on that long."

Fred laughed. "No, I promise. We do have some way to go, though. Fortunately, the distance that would take hours for our tiny rice grains to cover, we can do in a few steps. Also we don't have to worry about sinking or storms, which the passengers on those old ships definitely did."

Mercantilism and Self-Governance

They continued on the path, which wound slowly downward until, eventually, they dropped below the tree cover and could see the river down a slope to their right. They could hear the water lapping at rocks and roots of trees.

"It's now the 1600s—Columbus's expedition was more than a hundred years ago," Fred said.

"It was the Age of Exploration!" Emily added exuberantly.

"In that time, captains, crews, map makers, mathematicians, and astrologers had learned how to navigate the oceans much better. They could explore with more confidence. One well-known map maker, Amerigo Vespucci, returned from his expedition with the most detailed and accurate map of the new land. People started calling the land America, after this map maker. Emily, do you remember why people were so excited about exploring?"

"All kinds of reasons," she said. "The Pilgrims wanted to have a place to live how they wanted, without others trying to control them and tell them what to believe. Others wanted adventure and were excited about exploring the world. But at first, most wanted to get gold, tea, silk, and spices from China. These products

helped so many people live happier and healthier lives, and merchants got rich by selling these things to the people."

"But they didn't find China," Ethan smiled. "Instead, they discovered a new land and people. Surprise!"

"In many ways, America was even better than China because there was nearly endless land for planting valuable crops," Fred said. "Tobacco, potatoes, and more…. Remember, most of these colonies were sponsored by companies—royal companies that wanted to get rich."

"Royal companies?" Emily asked. "So these companies belonged to King James?"

"Some of them did." Fred hopped over a rock and reached level ground. "Remember talking about the feudal system where the king and his lords owned all the land and everyone else had to work like slaves for them?"

"Well, these kings and lords realized that controlling the farms and herds on their own land had its limitations. Trading like the merchants was where the real wealth was," he continued. "Now they wanted to control trade too. So they updated the feudal system and turned royal lords into royal merchant companies. These companies hatched a plan to get a lot of people to go farm all the new land in America. The plan was that they would

allow regular people to own land there, on the condition that all the crops that were harvested could only be sold back to the British merchants, at the price that they decided—and not to anyone else. This was a practice called *mercantilism*."

"And I'm guessing those merchants would then turn around and sell the crops for way more to get a profit," Ethan said.

"This is like the free trade system we talked about, isn't it?" Emily asked. She picked a bluebell from the side of the path. "Like in Italy?"

"Yes and no. This system does use trade,

but it isn't free for everyone. It's controlled by the king and his nobles," Fred replied.

Ethan ducked under a tree branch. "Why not let everyone be free to trade, like in Italy and the Silk Road?"

"Isn't it obvious?" Fred said, pausing to let the twins try to think of the answer. "The kings and lords wanted the peasant class to remain peasants, not become rich and free. They wanted to get rich off the backs of the people like they always had."

Fred stopped to rest. They'd been walking for some time now, and the day was hot.

"But all the new workers coming to

America… they were probably happy to do it because then they could actually own some land, right?" Emily asked.

"Sure," Fred agreed. "Even with mercantilism happening, the children of those workers wouldn't be low-class Englanders, living in slums; they would become respectable farmers and weavers and smiths. America, because of the liberty the new system allowed, became a place of opportunity." He stopped a moment to watch a sailboat whisk by, the small waves crashing white against her blue sides.

The twins saw what he was looking at and stopped too. "A sailboat," Emily said. "Like the *Mayflower*. Only way smaller."

"And slower. As fast as that boat seems to be going, the big sails of the *Mayflower* could move a ship much faster. But the ocean is far bigger than this river. So big, in fact, that it was almost impossible for the trading companies, and all of the Royal Navy, to enforce their agreements. The colonists learned to easily evade the clerks and customs officials and trade with whomever could give the best price."

"That's called *smuggling*," Emily said. "I read about that. Sounds fishy… and maybe a little fun." She had a mischievous smile.

"Well, there were plenty of people here to trade with, right?" Ethan said. "Not just the British… Fred's ship is Dutch, for example. And there were natives here already."

Fred waved them forward again, along the path. The twins bounced ahead a few yards and listened as Fred explained more. "You're right, Ethan. The Dutch, English, Spanish, and French—they were all here in America, in addition to the natives, importing, exporting, and trading with each other. Their different rulers back in Europe just couldn't control trade or tax these different colonies like they wanted to."

Emily found a log and was balancing her way across it, one foot in front of the other, with her arms spread out to her sides. "That sounds kind of like Italy," she said. "People got rich when they could work for their own benefit, trade with whom they wanted, and not be controlled by rulers."

"But all the trade must go through his majesty, the king!" Fred declared, pretending to be a Royal Navy captain.

"No, it doesn't," Ethan said, crouching and speaking in a whisper. "The king might *want* it to, but how can he stop us?" Ethan slipped behind a tree so smoothly that the trunk seemed to swallow him up. "Poof, I'm gone!"

"But I have armies and navies," Fred said, his voice regal and powerful. "I will catch you, you fiend!"

"Will you?" Ethan said. His voice now came from behind another tree. "Good luck!" He stepped back onto the path, a small smile on his face. "But just so we can make peace, I'll be glad to throw *some* of my trade your way, your majesty." He held out a packet of nuts and berries. "Snacks anyone?"

"We're about halfway," Fred announced, no longer in character, his hand resting on the side of the old pump house they had seen from the viewpoint at the beginning. "I think now would be a great time to talk about the destinations of our little rice ships and have a snack."

They sat against a cool stone while Ethan passed out the packets of food. Fred continued, "Remember, these voyagers knew that the trip would be very long, hard, and dangerous, and that some of them would probably not make it. People often died of exposure or illness along the way. Ethan, your ship made it safely to Virginia, and founded a colony named after the king."

Ethan thought for a moment. "King James, right? That's why the colony is Jamestown?"

"Correct. My Dutch colonists made it to the mouth of the Hudson River and founded their colony, New Amsterdam, on a long island there now called, not surprisingly, Long Island, New York."

"But Emily, things didn't go as planned for your ship. The *Mayflower* got blown seriously off course. Originally, the Plymouth Colony had a charter—a permission slip of sorts—to colonize Virginia as well. But they didn't land in Virginia."

"I know this part," Ethan said. "They landed in Massachusetts at Plymouth Rock, kind of by Boston."

"The only reason they had a ship to take them to America in the first place was because they made a deal with the Plymouth Company saying that they would plant and harvest crops for seven years to pay the company back. But because their charter was only supposed to be used for the land of Virginia, the group was worried that some of the passengers wouldn't keep their end of the bargain and run off. So they wanted to write a new agreement before they got off the boat. They probably didn't expect it to end up being so important."

Ethan took a sip from his water bottle. "That's the Mayflower Compact, right? You gave us copies of it, but I don't remember what it said."

Some non-religious passengers—called "Strangers"—felt that since the *Mayflower* had landed outside of Virginia, they were no longer bound to the company's rules and should be free to live freely and independently.

But religious Pilgrim leaders feared that without a government to enforce rules and make everyone work together, they would all die.

The group finally voted on a basic set of rules, and the Mayflower Compact was created. It was one of the first experiments in self-government in the New World.

"I sort of do," Emily said. "It was an agreement they voted on to keep everyone together and take care of each other so they could all survive, until they could set up a full government later."

"That's what makes the Mayflower Compact so important," replied Fred. "The Pilgrims independently formed new laws, without a king—just the way they wanted. The concept of self-government was an idea that changed the world."

"A new branch of the vine!" Ethan said.

"Over the next 200 years, other settlers would try the same thing. Think about how far away the hills were when we started."

"A long way," Ethan said. "A lot farther if I were sailing on a little grain of rice." Tree branches waved above his head, and a bird chirped in the brush a few yards off. They looked out toward the hills in the distance, which now didn't seem so far away.

Emily stretched her legs on the grass. "But it really was that far to America," she said. "When you left Europe, you knew you were probably never coming back. And you'd probably never hear from anyone from the old country again, especially if you were blown off course and landed in an unknown place. That sounds so scary!"

"You'd be by yourself," Ethan said. "It would basically be like colonizing Mars. You could say you were loyal to your government on Earth, but really... there's nobody there to control you. You could do whatever you wanted to. Freedom!"

"That's pretty close to what happened," Fred said. "Only a decade later, thousands of Puritans followed the Pilgrims to find religious freedom and new opportunity, settling a new colony in Boston. Before long, cargo ships from the Old World came to collect the large crops that were harvested and the exotic animal furs that were hunted. But for the most part, yes, the colonists got to do what they wanted. The ocean separating Europe from the Americas meant the colonists had to get pretty good at solving their own problems independently."

"And if someone didn't like the way their colony was being governed," he added, "they could just leave and start a new settlement—which happened a lot. The continent was so big that it would be two hundred years later before they knew how big it really was."

"It was still dangerous, though," Emily said. "Right? I mean, the land wasn't empty. There were people already here—all of the natives—and some of them thought the colonists were a threat to them."

"But some didn't." Ethan drew a picture in the dirt with a stick. It looked like a roasted bird. "Thanksgiving. There were some natives who helped the colonists."

Fred nodded. "Many of the natives were friendly, at least for as long as the colonists also were. Next leg of the journey?"

Ethan jumped up. "I'm ready."

More About Us!

Tisquantum
Patuxet tribe of Cape Cod

In 1614, "Squanto" and some of his people were captured by English explorers and brought to Europe to be slaves, but he was saved by a priest who taught him the English language. Years later, he returned home to find that his tribe had all died from disease.

Not long after, the Pilgrims arrived in Cape Cod. Squanto discovered the suffering colony, and because he could speak to them, he spent nearly two years teaching them about the area, how to build warm houses, grow and cook corn, and make peace with the native tribes.

William Bradford, leader of the colony, said that Squanto was sent to them by God.

Pocahontas
Powhatan Tribe of Virginia

The famous daughter of Chief Powhatan, who saved Captain John Smith from execution, was also friendly to other colonists of Jamestown—bringing them food and playing games with the children.

Later, there was fighting among her tribe and the colonists. Pocahontas was kidnapped and taken away from her people. At that time, she married John Rolfe and they had a son together. Eventually they traveled to London where she met with royalty and reconnected with John Smith. Sadly, Pocahontas fell ill and died just before they would return to Virginia.

More Colonies

The twins climbed a little hill and the path leveled out. They walked for another hour. The trees thinned and a meadow appeared to their right, spread out with wild grass, bluebells, and buttercups waving in the breeze. Ethan and Emily were holding their grains of rice out, imagining ships from royal companies sailing on the seemingly endless water toward Virginia.

Judging by the cars they could hear passing by just out of sight, they weren't far from their destination now. There came a whiff of hot dogs from a cart in the park by the bridge. Fred caught up with the twins and the three walked together for a moment. "Each colony had its own ideas about how to run things. In Massachusetts, for example, they were very strict about keeping the Puritan religion, well... pure. They were so strict that they kicked out two people—Roger Williams and Anne Hutchinson—who believed something different. Those two

went down the coast a little way and formed another colony that they called Rhode Island."

"Wait, what?" Emily groaned. "You mean after all that effort to seek religious freedom, they wouldn't even allow it for others in their own colonies?"

"I thought all this time they were the good guys," Ethan said.

"It's not that simple, Ethan," Fred replied. He stopped in front of the twins and crouched down so that their heads were on the same level. "This is a very important thing I want you to remember through all of these lessons."

The twins had never heard him so serious. "When you view history through the lens of good guys and bad guys, you're missing the point. In England, George Washington is the 'bad guy' and King George is the 'good guy.'"

"So it depends on where you're standing?" Emily asked.

"Think of it this way," Fred said. "It doesn't help us learn much from history to simply say that this person was bad and that one was good. These religious settlers did some things we might want to copy. Many of them were courageous. They were willing to sacrifice for what they believed. But some of them also did things we might *not* want to copy—like making a rigid religious government that didn't always value freedom of speech. Rather than call them the good guys or the bad guys, what could we do when we learn about the things they did?"

Ethan thought for a moment. "We could see if we agree with them. We could judge their actions by the Golden Rule."

"We could see if their decisions made things better or worse," Emily added, her eyes off toward the horizon. "Then we can decide whether or not we want to copy those decisions in our day."

Fred straightened up and stretched. "I'm proud of you both. Too often, people read history in order to judge people, rather than to understand them. It's a pleasure to have you as my companions on this journey."

He shaded his eyes and gazed down the path. "We're making good time," he said. "But our ships' journeys aren't quite finished. And there are other colonies, too, where things were a little different.

Mine became New York when the British took it over, but you know what? The Dutch citizens didn't care that much, because whichever government flew their flags over their cities were so far away that it didn't really matter enough to fight about it. But then William Penn's—"

"Is that the guy who founded Pennsylvania?" Emily asked.

"It is, yes," Fred confirmed. "Those colonies were much more welcoming of different religions, but struggled with understanding liberty in other ways. And Ethan's was one of the most unruly. Being right in the middle of the colonies, Virginia was unique."

"Good thing, too," Ethan said. "Because some really important Founding Fathers came from there, right?"

"True enough," Fred said. "But that generation won't be born for many more years. We'll talk about those men another time."

They finally reached the fork in the path. One led to the playground, and the other to the parking lot where Mr. and Mrs. Tuttle were waiting. A huge excavator was removing that part of the fork, surrounded by caution tape and a group of workers hauling wheelbarrows.

One of them came over. "Sorry, folks," she said. "If you're going to the parking lot, you'll have to go around through the playground. We're re-paving the path here."

"A detour," Emily said. "Just like what happened to the *Mayflower*."

"I hope it's not *just* like the *Mayflower*," Ethan said. "I don't think Fred would be too happy about having to live at a playground, even if he got to invent his own government."

Fred laughed. "It's worse than that. If we don't get back to the parking lot, your parents won't know where to pick us up. They're taking us out for ice cream!"

The twins heard that and exchanged a look. They sprinted off on the detour through the playground without even checking to see if Fred was coming along. His laughter floated after them.

More About This!

The African Slave Trade In America

European explorers and colonists were not the only people who came to the New World. Some were brought against their will.

From the very beginning of the exploration of the Americas, it was common practice to capture native people. The Spanish and Portuguese would force them to work in their gold and silver mines. In addition to this slavery, there were also indentured servants who were made to work for a period of time to pay off debts.

Many people began to rely heavily on this labor force: people who came to grow crops, collect animal pelts, and harvest natural resources for their kings, as well as the company shareholders who helped finance these expeditions. Their reliance grew so much that their appetite for more slaves expanded the market for slavery, where people would capture and sell Africans to traders to be sold in the American colonies. (It was even common for African people to do the capturing and selling of other Africans.) These captured individuals were chained to the floors of the hulls of large slave ships as they crossed the Atlantic Ocean. In these barbaric conditions, it was common that half of the captives would die on the voyage. Millions died in this way. Even so, millions more Africans survived the voyage to become slaves in Brazil and the Caribbean.

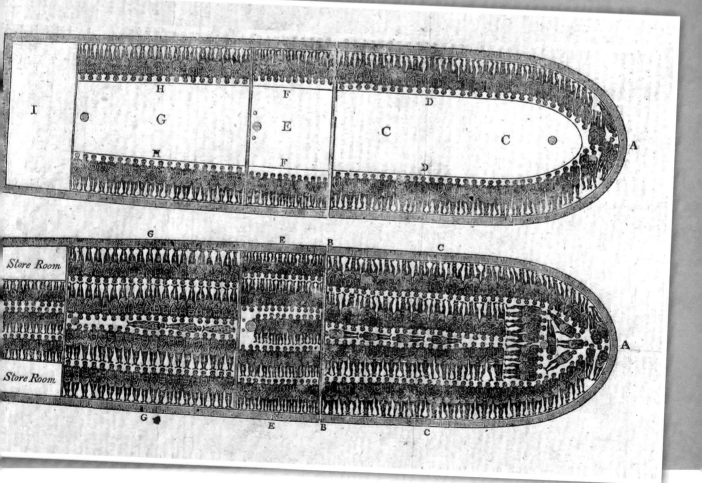

In 1619, a year before Pilgrims landed at Plymouth, a Dutch ship called the *White Lion* attacked a Portuguese slave ship called the *San Juan Bautista*, taking some of the African captives to work for Dutch and English forts in North America. About 20 Africans were taken to Point Comfort, Virginia to be sold as indentured servants to colonists in Jamestown. This was the beginning of a practice that would get worse and worse over the years in the North American colonies.

Initially, indentured servants had some legal rights. After years of labor, they were legally entitled to be freed, and their children were never permitted to be born as property. But by the 1640s, it had become common to keep African slaves and never free them. (Massachusetts was the first colony to recognize legal slavery in 1640.) Then in 1662, a Virginia law made it so that the children of enslaved mothers were property of slave owners, too!

With all of these slaves at their disposal, tobacco and rice plantation owners were able to greatly expand their harvest. Royal companies rewarded them with more land and wealth. This encouraged an appetite for even more slaves. Eventually, enslaved Africans became a significant portion of the population, especially in the southern agricultural colonies of North America.

The awful institution of slavery was customary throughout all of history, and in almost all cultures on earth. This practice went on for hundreds of years in America, until the Thirteenth Amendment to the U.S. Constitution was ratified in 1865.

2. Massachusetts

The settlements in Plymouth (1620) and Boston (1630) encouraged over 20,000 Puritans to immigrate from England to the area by 1640. Th[e] authoritarian governance of John Winthrop caused some to flee to Connecticut and Rhode Island for more freedom.

3. New York

It was originally called New Amsterdam by Dutch settlers (1625), until the people allowed England to take over without a fight (1664), renaming it after the King's brother. Because of i[ts] harbors and river access, New York became a great center fo[r] business and culture.

4. Maryland

Lord George Calvert sought to establish a colony of refuge fo[r] persecuted Catholics in Englan[d.] He found a location at the hea[d] of the Chesapeake Bay. George['s] son received permission from King Charles I in 1632, and his grandson became Maryland's first governor.

Settlement Timeline

1. Virginia

Though the Jamestown settlement first started in 1607, the Virginia colony had great difficulties until Pocahontas's husband, John Rolfe, developed the tobacco industry (1612), and the colony formed the first representative self-government, the House of Burgesses (1619).

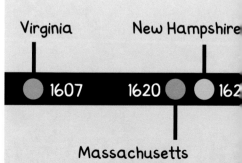

Virginia   New Hampshire

1607   1620   162[4]

Massachusetts

RHODE ISLAND

...nished from Massachusetts
...proposing religious freedom,
...perty rights for natives, and
...t churches shouldn't control
...ernments, Roger Williams
...unded this new colony (1636).
...ilarly, Anne Hutchinson was
...o expelled and found a home
...his new colony of freedom.

CONNECTICUT

...omas Hooker founded the
...ony (1636) after dissenting
...h Puritan leaders in Boston
...out religious freedom and
...ting rights for non-Puritans.
...e Fundamental Orders of
...nnecticut may be the world's
...t written constitution for a
...resentative government.

DELAWARE

...utch trading post populated
...Swedish settlers in 1631, this
...gion came under British control
...en the Duke of York gained
...ntrol of the Dutch settlements.
...ter, William Penn was given
...e land, and for decades both
...onies remained under the
...me government.

8. NEW HAMPSHIRE

Although the area was settled
by Massachusetts fishermen
in 1623, it remained under that
colony's control until 1741 when
King George II finally gave them
their own governorship, with
Benning Wentworth being the first
to fill the position.

9. NORTH CAROLINA

Multiple parties were sent to this
land as early as 1585, but those
settlers mysteriously vanished!
Later, in 1663, the territory was
named for Charles I (Carolina is
Latin for Charles) by eight British
nobles. In 1729, the population
grew rapidly, encouraging a split
of the North and South colonies.

10. SOUTH CAROLINA

Plantation owners from the
Caribbean came to this region
to grow tobacco and cotton.
They brought in slave ships, and
the government gave away free
land with every slave purchased.
It was a race to own the most
slaves! Both Carolinas were
made royal colonies in 1729.

11. NEW JERSEY

Eight years after the Duke of
York had been given control of
New Amsterdam (now New York),
he split off the southern area to
be controlled by his friends, Lord
John Berkeley and Sir George
Carteret. They were given a
Royal charter for colonization in
1702.

12. PENNSYLVANIA

As a friend of King George II,
William Penn asked to establish
a colony for his religious group
called the Quakers, for an
experiment of religious freedom
and peace among different
people—including natives! He was
given a royal land grant to start
his colony in 1681.

13. GEORGIA

This Royal colony was founded
by James Oglethorpe in 1732 to
give people an opportunity to
pay off their debtors who were
threatening them with prison in
England. Georgia also provided
a welcome military buffer for
the English colonies from the
Spanish in Florida.

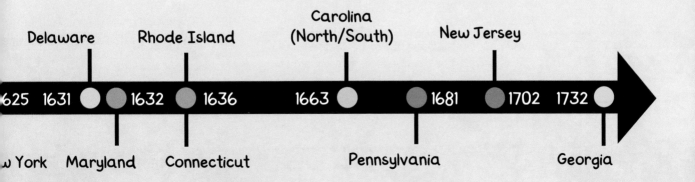

A Thought From Connor

One of the problems in learning about the past is judging people based on our knowledge and ideas today. We sometimes think ourselves as so much more educated and moral and, in light of that, we look down on people in the past for their bad decisions or imperfections.

I think that's the case with how many people look at some of the Puritans. How ironic—hypocritical, even—to demand religious freedom for yourselves and then not provide it to others who think differently from you.

It's like we saw in the last chapter—ideas that are different from the majority are often seen as problematic. Dissent isn't tolerated well by those in power. And when a minority group suddenly becomes a majority (because you're the only group around for hundreds of miles on an unfamiliar continent), it then imposes its own restrictions on contrarian ideas expressed by the minority within that group.

Humans aren't perfect, so as we look at history we have to afford people a measure of grace. It's hard to suddenly come into power and then "practice what you preach"; too many are tempted to use their power to serve their own interests and enforce their ideas on everyone else.

I think this pattern offers us a lot to think about in our own day about people who have different ideas, and how important it is for us to be consistent and not hypocritical. It's harder than it sounds!

History is great for this exact reason—that we can see other's mistakes and learn from them, so we can improve ourselves. The point isn't to judge people in the past; we should see what they did wrong and think about how we can avoid repeating those problems today.

Keep this in mind as we continue in the chapters ahead. There will be a lot of mistakes and problems to learn from!

Let's Talk About It!

If you could choose anything to eat for breakfast, what would you choose? Some days you might prefer eggs and toast, another day fruit, but let's be honest, some days you might choose to eat a stack of delicious peanut butter cups!

Which choices are the best ones? That's actually not an easy question to answer. It's true that eating candy for breakfast might not give you the best nutrients, but maybe it's your birthday. Maybe it would cheer you up if you're feeling sad. Or, what if you literally have nothing else to eat?! You see, that's a choice that you (and your parents) need to be free to make—because only you fully understand your situation.

The British government thought they could make the best decisions for the settlers who lived thousands of miles away. But if those colonists obeyed those laws, dictating who they could and couldn't trade with, they might not have even survived.

Consider this question: Do you think governments today can do a better job than you at deciding what you should do with your life?

Or, how about this: What are the negative consequences when the government controls what medicines you must take or are not allowed to take? What if they want to control where you can travel, what size your house must be, what kind of car you are allowed to drive, how children must be educated, or, in some countries, how many children you can have?

Is there any circumstance in which your life would be better if the government made these decisions for you instead of you making them for yourself?

Chapter 4

The Dawn of Human Rights

Framing the Past

Mrs. Tuttle woke her twins before the sun was up. Still groggy, Ethan rolled over and asked, "Whaaa?"

"Get up," his mother said. Her face was barely lit by the nightlight next to Ethan's bed. She smiled gently and shook Ethan's shoulder again, not letting him go back to sleep.

A shadow moved into the doorway of the room. Emily's sleepy face peered in. "If I have to get up, so do you," she said. "It's only fair."

But Ethan was already swinging his legs off the bed and climbing to his feet. He looked at the clock on his nightstand. The first number was a 4. He blinked a few times to make sure that's what he saw. "Why do we have to get up so early?" he moaned.

"We got a text message from Fred last night after you both went to bed," Mrs. Tuttle answered. "He has something to show you, but you won't be able to see it once the sun rises. But if it's too much trouble, I'll just call him and tell him—"

"No!" both twins said at once. All of a sudden, Ethan found he was wide awake. Emily dashed back to her room to change clothes.

"It's a little chilly, so put on a jacket," Mrs. Tuttle said. She held one out for each of the kids as they hustled out the door. "Fred said he'll be waiting for you at the dike." That was only a few blocks away. They could be there in a few minutes.

Each of their bikes had powerful LED lights on the front and back so cars could see them, except there weren't any cars on the roads this early. Even if there had been, the lights could be seen for a mile.

"I wonder what we look like," Emily said. "Some kind of UFO, I bet." She crossed the road to look over at Ethan. "Yep. You're an alien, all right."

"Take me to your leader," Ethan said in a robotic voice. "Isn't that what you're supposed to say if you're an alien?"

"How would I know?" Emily said. "I don't hang out with people from other planets. But I'll take you to our leader—and I'll get there first too!" Emily leaned forward and shot off into the dark, with Ethan watching her UFO lights bounce ahead of him.

The morning sky seemed darker than when they went to sleep. No moon shone, and the wind was still. Spoonerville seemed like a ghost town. Ethan pedaled faster and came up even with Emily. "It's kind of like we're the only two people here," he said. "Maybe this is what it felt like to be the first settlers in America."

They rounded the curve in front of the Nguyen's home. Emily waved to her friend Helen's dark window, though Helen was surely fast asleep—and there in front of them was the dike. But Fred was

nowhere to be seen. The long, grassy hill that protected the city from the seasonal flooding of the river was just as still and dark as the rest of the town, but then they saw, way out in the middle, a dark shape swinging a lantern. The sparkling light winked at them, and the twins pushed their bikes up the incline to find Fred half-covered by a blanket, looking through a telescope.

"Welcome, my friends," he said. "I'm glad you were willing to have an early morning adventure with me. I hope to show you something you've never seen before—and also talk a little about the next stage in colonial history."

"What are you looking at?" Ethan said. He set his bike down on the grass. It was fresh-cut and smelled like summer, even though the morning was cool.

"Just look off to the northeast for a minute. You'll see it without the telescope."

For a long minute, the twins scanned the sky, but all they saw were the twinkling stars. "The big dipper is easy to find, and that's Cassiopeia, but I don't—"

"What was that?" Emily softly shouted, pointing. A streak of light had crossed the dark velvet sky like a bullet and faded away. It had taken less than a second.

"Shooting star," Ethan said. His voice was filled with wonder. "But that was one of the biggest—"

"Another one!" Emily said. "What are the chances of two in just one minute?"

Fred chuckled. "Pretty good, actually.

This is one of the biggest meteor showers in the sky. It's called the Perseid meteor shower—an annual fireworks show from the heavens because of a nearby comet that bears your name: Swift-Tuttle." He smiled seeing the twins' faces light up. "The best time to see the show is in the very early morning, like this."

The twins gasped as more meteorites streaked overhead. Fred told them to come and look through his telescope. "You miss a few this way, but the ones you do see through the lens are incredible."

Sure enough, Emily saw one right away in the telescope's eyepiece. It was so big! She had never seen one so well before. Ethan took a little longer, but the one he saw lit up the whole sky. He could see the rock breaking up, making sparks off the tail like a sparkler on Independence Day.

"This is amazing," Emily said. "We're so lucky!"

"Not much of it is luck," Fred said, sitting back in a lawn chair and making a box with his fingers in front of his face. "If you know what, where, and when to look, you can find all sorts of things other people might miss. Framing the sky this way is the same with framing history. If you want to understand the lessons of the past, and not just memorize names, dates, and battles, you need to know where and when to look to find the best view."

"But there are billions of events in history. How can you know what to look for?" Ethan asked. He hadn't taken his eye from the telescope for a while, hoping to catch just one more shooting star.

"One of the best ways to investigate a mystery is to work backward. The story of America is the result of a long struggle between power and liberty. The oppression of rulers goes back longer than recorded history, but the ideas of human rights, as we know them today, really started with the English Magna Carta of 1215."

Emily tapped Ethan on the shoulder and took his place at the telescope. Ethan said, "The 1200s? Hey, isn't that the century of Marco Polo?"

"Very good, Ethan. The King of England at the time, King John, upset his feudal landlords—the barons. They refused to protect him from invading armies or collect taxes from their peasants unless he signed a charter, the Magna Carta, guaranteeing their rights, and giving them power to help make decisions about the government. It was the first English parliament. The king had to admit that he couldn't just do whatever he wanted without the consent of the lords. But those rights didn't apply to everyone quite yet."

England's Royal Problem

"But," Fred continued, "Europe's feudal systems were falling apart. Do you remember why?"

"For starters, it was awful," Emily said. "Everyone was basically a slave, forced to work for the king's benefit. But also because of books... regular people were learning that just because you were king, doesn't mean you can do whatever you wanted. They were starting to think for themselves!"

Fred came over to the telescope and adjusted it to point a little more east. Then he sat back down. Another handful of meteors burned through the atmosphere.

They were beautiful, and so bright in the darkness. "While we watch for more shooting stars, let me tell you the story of not-so-merry old England in the 1600s."

"Over a hundred years since Columbus! Still the Age of Exploration, right?" Emily asked.

"The pilgrims had started a colony in Plymouth..." Ethan added.

"Yes, yes, but hold on," Fred replied. "The story starts just after the Pilgrims landed in Plymouth, but just like knowing where and when to see meteors, if you want to know why things happened in America, you need to know what was happening in England at the same time."

Timeline
European Religious Wars

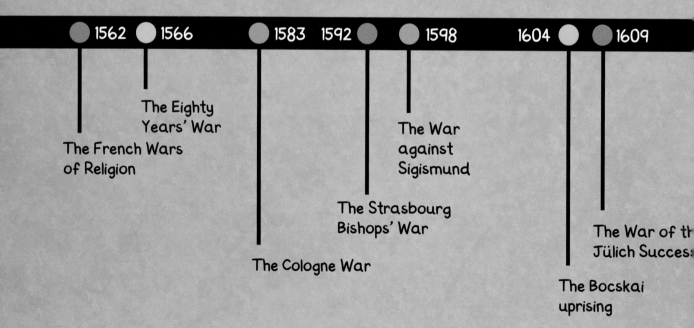

1562 1566 1583 1592 1598 1604 1609

The Eighty Years' War

The French Wars of Religion

The War against Sigismund

The Strasbourg Bishops' War

The Cologne War

The War of the Jülich Succession

The Bocskai uprising

The twins lay down on the cool grass and let Fred's voice roll over them as they watched the sky above.

"Turns out the Pilgrims left just in time. Bloody religious wars between the Catholics and Protestants were creating turmoil throughout Europe," he said. "Kings were losing power because people were more concerned with what they believed God's laws were than what their king's laws were. Also, England had created its own church, remember? The Anglican Church, where the king was the head of both the government *and* the church. Remember that King James even made his own version of the Bible? What the king said was now both legal law and religious law. No appeal, no argument. Even the people's elected representatives in Parliament couldn't vote against the decisions of the king, whether they liked them or not. The king's power was absolute again!"

"But some people found their religious beliefs on the list of things that would not be allowed—"

"Like the Pilgrims," Emily said. "The ones on the *Mayflower*." She zipped up her jacket. A slight breeze had begun to blow. The show in the sky never slowed, but in the east a thin line of brighter sky had begun to grow. The sun would end the performance pretty soon.

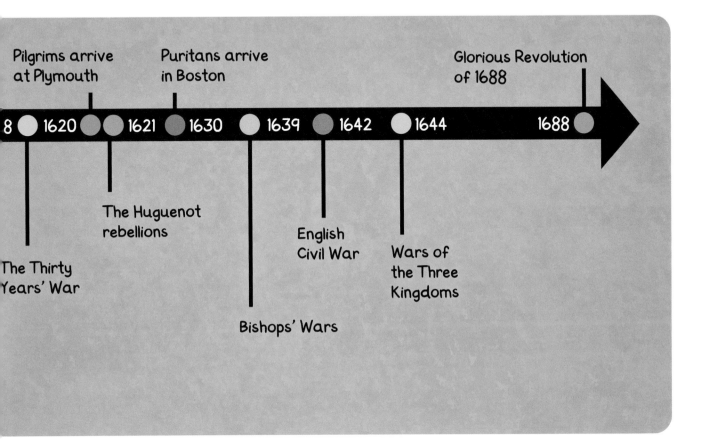

Pilgrims arrive at Plymouth

Puritans arrive in Boston

Glorious Revolution of 1688

8　1620　　1621　1630　1639　1642　1644　1688

The Huguenot rebellions

English Civil War

Wars of the Three Kingdoms

The Thirty Years' War

Bishops' Wars

"Only five years after those Pilgrims settled in Massachusetts, King James died, and left the kingdom to his son Charles I, who did very much the same as his father, making himself absolute ruler, ignoring the lords in Parliament and persecuting Puritans for criticizing the Anglican Church. Eventually, Parliament and the poor and persecuted people from around the country joined together and created an army. They were called the Parliamentarians."

"What could they do? Didn't King James have 'absolute' power?" Ethan asked, making air quote signs with his fingers.

"Well, Parliamentarians fought a civil war against the king and his loyal subjects, the Royalists. The Parliamentarians won the war and took the king to court, found him guilty of treason, then chopped off his head," Fred said matter-of-factly, watching the reaction on Ethan's face.

"I guess his 'absolute' power was all in his head," Emily smirked, copying Ethan's air quotes. "Until he lost it, that is! I've never heard of a king's subjects beheading their king before."

"It was a pretty significant event that made the other monarchs of Europe take notice. Other kings with delusions of absolute power were forced to recognize that their power was actually limited to what their subjects would allow."

"So who controlled the English government after that?" Emily asked.

As king, I have absolute authority over you!

Wanna bet?

Royalists ("Cavaliers") Parliamentarians ("Roundheads")

More About Us!

James I 1566 – 1625
First king to rule Scotland and England. Internal conflicts with Catholics and Puritans strained his rule. Sponsored a translation of the Bible.

Charles I 1600 – 1649
Forced his religion on the Scots, starting a war. Attempted to arrest dissenting voices of Parliament. Was beheaded for abusing his power.

Cromwell 1599 – 1658
Declared Britain a republic called the Commonwealth. A brutal dictator until his death. His son, Richard, renounced power, restoring the monarchy.

Charles II 1630 – 1685
Was on good behavior with Parliament. Navigated the internal strife better than previous rulers. Set up free religious colonies in America.

James II 1633 – 1701
Married a Catholic and made reforms for Catholics. He had a son who became Catholic, causing both Anglicans and Puritans to allow his dethroning.

"For a while, England was a sort of republic. Laws were made by councils of the people. But it didn't last very long because they did a pretty awful job, too—now persecuting the Catholics and Anglicans for *their* religious beliefs and still trying to control everyone and everything. So then Charles II, the son of the beheaded king, promised that he would be a good and mild king, and the Parliament allowed him to take the throne."

"Wait," Emily said. "Doesn't this always happen in stories? Someone promises that they'll be different, but once they get what they want, they never follow through."

"In *stories*?" Ethan reacted. "It sounds like every single election with fake promises from politicians!"

Fred chuckled. "It does, doesn't it? And you've guessed it. Even though Charles II *was* nicer to both Puritans and Catholics, every time he disagreed with Parliament, he just dissolved it and sent everyone home. He ruled for 25 years as another absolute monarch—a king with total power, even though he saw his father beheaded for doing some of the same things. After Charles died without legitimate heirs to take his place as king, the throne went to his brother, James II."

"Was James II any better?" Emily asked.

"He may have been, but that didn't matter to Parliament."

"I don't get it. Why would being a nicer king not matter?"

"Well, he was Catholic and his wife gave birth to a son, the future king, who would also be raised Catholic. And for Parliament, that was something they couldn't take any more. They really, really didn't want the Pope and the Catholic church to control their country."

"Ugh!" Ethan sighed. "Most of the violence is because everyone was trying to force their religious beliefs on everyone else? Why didn't someone just say, 'Hey let's let everyone believe what they want!'?"

"There were people who said that..." Emily remembered. "They had left to go to Holland!"

"Excellent, Emily." Fred went on, "Holland was a place known for its tolerance of religion, ideas, and culture. That's why the Puritan Pilgrims stayed there for a while. But many different kinds of people took shelter there too."

"With all those different people, I bet there were a lot of different opinions," Ethan said.

"There were, for sure, but sometimes different opinions can help people think more deeply. John Locke was a young man when Charles I was... uh... separated from his head. He observed, firsthand, this tumultuous time in England's history. He thought about what brought prosperity, peace, and harmony between

More About Me!

John Locke
1632 - 1734

After performing life-saving surgery on Lord Ashley's infected liver, Locke was hired as his personal physician, and was also introduced to Ashley's political views and inner circle—advocating for rights for British citizens and limitations on monarchical power.

When an assassination attempt was made on King James II, he suspected that leaders of this movement were responsible. Locke fled to Holland, where he spent years writing out these new ideas about liberty and the limitations of government authority. These writings inspired many great thinkers, especially the American founders as they wrote the Declaration of Independence. He is sometimes known as the "Father of Liberalism."

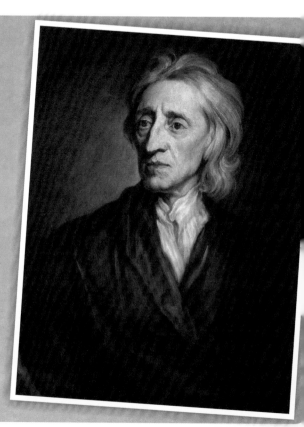

people, and what brought poverty, chaos, and war. Who had the right to rule? What gave them that right? How could people be free to follow their own ideas and get along with their neighbors who believed differently?"

"For him to write what he wanted without being arrested for it, he also had to leave for Holland."

The twins got up to overlook the river flowing smoothly on the other side of the dike. The light was growing, and the stars began to fade out into a wide, pale blue sky. It was harder and harder to see the shooting stars.

The Glorious Revolution

Fred joined them to watch the sunrise. "Like those shooting stars, the ideas of John Locke—and many other thinkers of the time—lit up the minds of men. But unlike those meteors, they didn't burn out. Once a person's mind catches fire with the ideas of liberty, it's almost impossible to extinguish."

Emily thought for a moment. "During the Protestant Reformation, people started reading the Bible for themselves, which made them want to live according to their own beliefs. How are John Locke's ideas different?"

"I think I know," Ethan answered. "Most people were focused on the freedom to choose for themselves... but they didn't always allow that freedom for others. Some people wanted to force their countrymen to believe or behave exactly like them... or else! That's not liberty."

"Excellent observation, Ethan," Fred said. "Locke wrote about an idea that was pretty new and radical at the time—that the government's job was to protect everyone's right to life, liberty, and property. Equal liberty for all! And these ideas were well received by some members of the British Parliament who wanted to change things. They called themselves Whigs."

"It wasn't easy, though," he added. "Change never is. And one of those changes came about in England in 1688."

"The Glorious Revolution of 1688?" Ethan asked. He looked over at Fred, whose eyebrows were raised in surprise. Ethan shrugged. "Our dad was talking to a friend of his last week about it, but I don't know what it means."

Fred laughed. "Your father is a very interesting man. This is the Glorious Revolution—but not the revolution we usually talk about in America—and we're going to talk about the bill of rights—but not the one Americans think of."

"I'm ready to hear how this story ends,"

Emily said. "How did England fix their king problem?"

"Well they definitely took a big step in the right direction," Fred said. "Almost everyone was upset with James II, even though he had only taken the throne a year or so earlier."

"And also he was Catholic," Ethan reminded them.

"Right," Fred continued. "Regardless of that, England had experienced a century of turmoil, with never-ending religious and civil war. The people were tired and ready for stability, but they were never going to go back to being subjects the way they had been. So a few Whigs and other like-minded nobles got together, and instead of fighting another civil war, they wrote to James II's daughter, Princess Mary, who had married Prince William of Orange in Holland."

As if on cue, the sun peeked over the horizon, shooting warm orange light on the dike, and casting long shadows behind them. "Since everything looks orange now, let me ask... why did they call him Orange?" Ethan said.

"Orange was a small principality in southern France. His father was Prince of Orange before he died, but his mother was the daughter of King Charles the headless. William was born in Holland and had been living there—"

"So far, this sounds like a good idea," Emily said. "Dutch people seemed to have some sense in the 1600s."

"Also he was Protestant, not Catholic," Fred said, looking over at Ethan. "The nobles invited Mary and her husband William to come and take the throne of England and the people banished James II instead of chopping off his head. William and Mary were welcomed as King and Queen of England, under one condition."

"What condition?" the twins asked.

"The ideas that men like Locke had shared through their writings had spread widely," Fred replied. "Now the people wanted guarantees of their rights—and on paper."

"Is it the bill of rights you said we were going to talk about?" Emily asked.

"It is. The English Bill of Rights protects the rights of Englishmen to a speedy trial, to keep arms for their defense, and other things that may sound familiar to you."

"The American Bill of Rights also has those things in it," Emily said. "Did theirs have something to do with ours?"

"Of course," Fred replied. "Many of the rights in *our* Bill of Rights are the same ones guaranteed to Englishmen. But ours has a very important difference, one we'll have to talk about another time."

"So *that's* what the Glorious Revolution of 1688 was!" Ethan said. "When the English finally demanded their rights."

More About This!
The English Bill of Rights

In 1689, Parliament, with both Tories and Whigs participating, created the Bill of Rights—a new law that contained the terms of their offer to William III and Mary II to rule as joint sovereigns.

This document guaranteed certain civil rights, including the rights to free elections, to petition the government, to own weapons for defense, and the prohibition of cruel and unusual punishment and excessive bail.

It set out the rights of Parliament to meet often and freely voice opposing opinions without threat of punishment. It gave all taxing and spending powers to Parliament—including the power to fund the King's army. It also set limitations on the monarchy.

Five hundred years earlier, a document called the Magna Carta first contemplated a world where law superseded the whims of the King, but with the English Bill of Rights, it was finally recognized and made law. The King had to listen to Parliament and respect the rights of the people. England now had a truly constitutional monarchy, rather than a king ruling on the pretext of divine right.

Fred nodded. "Almost no blood was shed in this revolution—that's pretty glorious, you have to admit. And this time, King William kept his promise to rule with justice and to be lenient to other religions. He granted the people more rights than they'd ever had, possibly anywhere on earth."

The sun was fully risen. It was a beautiful morning. The birds in the trees had begun to sing, and, every so often, a car went by on the road. But the twins didn't want to leave just yet.

"What happened in the colonies while all this was going on?" Ethan asked. "It must have been pretty hard to be all the way over here while so much was happening in England."

"No doubt it was," Fred said, folding up his chair and stowing it in a canvas bag. "The colonists couldn't do much about the constant wars and changes of king and government. But they were mostly left alone for almost a hundred and fifty years. So they had to learn to govern themselves. The new King and Whig Parliament were happy to let that continue. No two colonies did it quite the same way—they had quite a lot of imagination!—but all the colonies set up councils, assemblies, or legislatures of some kind to make laws for the citizens of that area. Later, they also became heavily influenced by Locke's writings, and they studied and thought about what the English Bill of Rights meant for them—after all, they believed themselves to be English citizens."

Emily helped unscrew the telescope and pack it into a padded black case to keep it safe. It was heavy! "If most of the people in the colonies were English," she said, "wouldn't those rights belong to them, too?"

"They would," Fred agreed.

"But what if the royal governors in charge of the colonies didn't behave like William and Mary?" Ethan said. "After all, they're a long way from England."

"You hit the nail on the head, Ethan. Some of the governors tried to behave like kings themselves. Many colonies rebelled against them. One famous rebellion was led by a man named Nathaniel Bacon, who wanted to set up a free government in Virginia with no king at all."

"That sounds like the American Revolution!" Ethan said. He folded up the telescope tripod.

"A hundred years early," Fred replied, clipping the telescope case closed. "As it turns out, the colonies still weren't ready for independence. Locke's ideas about individual liberty, equal rights, and representative government were just starting to bud on our history vine. They hadn't had time to grow and spread in the minds of the colonists.

"Those are long vines to grow so many miles across the sea," Ethan said. "But I guess if the ideas are strong enough, they'll grow pretty fast."

They helped Fred carry his gear back to his car, then the twins fetched their bikes.

Emily was so intrigued by what she was learning. "Now that we know about the Glorious Revolution, we're ready to talk about the American Revolution. That's next in our lessons, right?"

"Not yet," Fred said. "We do have to talk about a war, yes, the first world war."

"World War I?" Ethan asked. "That's not right. The Revolution comes before World War I."

"Yes," Fred said, climbing into his car and starting the engine. "But the first truly world war was fought long before either of them. Of course," he said, shifting into reverse, "we didn't call it a world war here in the colonies."

Without another word, he winked at the twins and backed out of his parking space. The twins watched his tail lights going down the street far in the distance. Then he was gone. They were quiet for a moment.

"That man sure can leave you wanting more," Ethan said.

Emily yawned. "What I want more of right now is my bed. I'm tired!"

Let's Talk About It!

It's tempting to want to look at history and classify people as *good* or *bad*, depending on what they did and how we feel about it today. Ethan and Emily are facing that same struggle and wanting to easily understand who was right and wrong based on how they acted.

Imagine you were the King of England at the time. You're the head of the Anglican Church, which was set up, in part, to create more order and separate the country from the control of the Pope. But now there are Puritans causing division, too—so you face problems both outside your country and within. Perhaps you're nervous about maintaining control.

So, why exactly might you be worried about the Puritans criticizing your church and authority? Or what concerns would you have about Catholics in your country who were gaining power in the government? After all, when these oppressed people were in power, sometimes they were as bad, or worse!

Do you think that the royal rulers had a valid reason to be concerned?

It's true that these kings, and many others in power, did some bad things. (The same is true of those in our government today...) They definitely oppressed the Puritans and Catholics. But even if they had a valid reason, can people have "order" or be united if they are forced by the government to be part of the same church?

Can you really change someone's beliefs through force anyway?

More importantly for us today, as we review the decisions of today's rulers, does it help us to understand their reasons for why they are doing the things they are? Is there something more to be learned than whether someone is a "good guy" or "bad guy"? Or should we instead focus on whether the actions themselves are good or bad?

How would you have done things differently to have a better result?

King John refusing to sign the Magna Carta when first presented to him

A Thought From Elijah

The Magna Carta, meaning "The Great Charter," was one of the first times that the concept of legal rights was written down. But as we learned in this chapter, that agreement between the King and the barons didn't work so well. Why not?

It wasn't until the ideas of liberty were more fully understood, thanks primarily to the teachings of John Locke, that people were able to realize why protecting one another's rights was so important. After a hundred years of turmoil and war, they finally prioritized and valued their rights more than their loyalty to the monarchy and demanded there be a Bill of Rights to clearly limit the government's power.

Today, our rights are threatened in a similar way. Not so much because the Constitution itself has changed, but more because most people do not cherish or even understand the philosophy of liberty that has brought about generations of peace and prosperity like never before in history. Words on a paper only go so far; what matters more are the ideas in people's hearts and minds, and whether they are willing to defend them when challenged by those in power.

When I look around during each election season, I often see a lot of people following the opinions of their preferred political "leaders," but if you understand liberty and value it, you can make your own judgments about political issues regardless of what people in power want you to think.

The Magna Carta was in many respects a revolutionary document and a beacon of hope in the beginning of the quest for liberty. But whether we're talking about the Magna Carta, the Constitution, or any other important document that claims to guarantee our rights, it's difficult to expect these "parchment barriers" to protect against the "spirit of power," as James Madison once said.

These important documents will ultimately fail if the people do not value their rights and honor the rights of others.

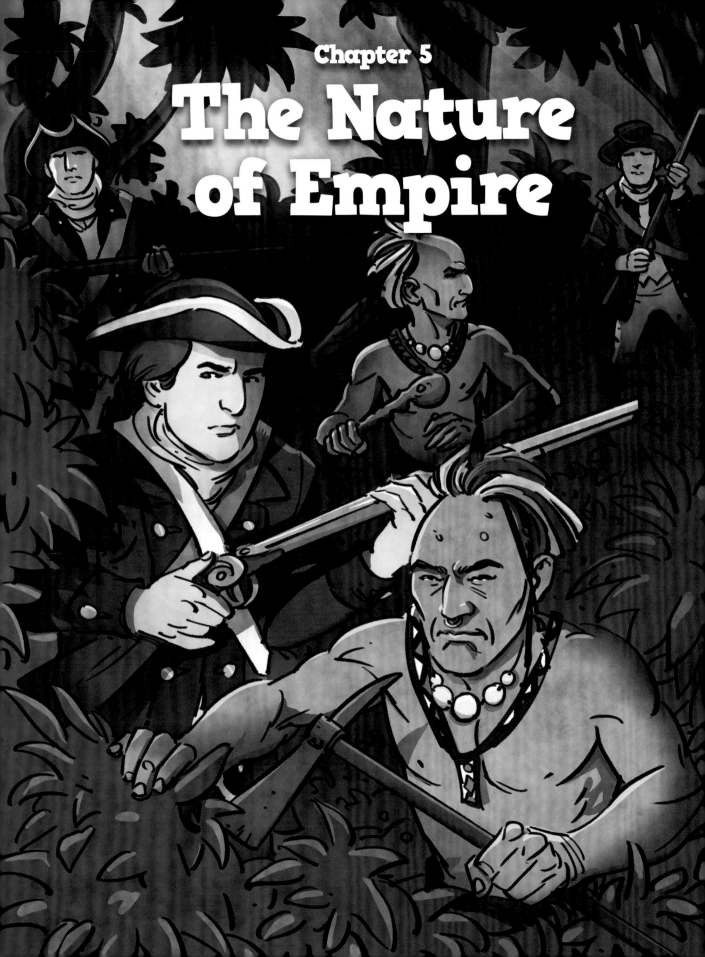

Chapter 5
The Nature of Empire

A World of Warring Empires

Emily poked at the packages. They squished under her finger. Whatever was underneath the brown butcher paper wasn't stiff like a box. "They're pretty soft."

"Chores first, packages can be opened after." Mrs. Tuttle crossed her arms and stood over them like a guard.

When you're excited about a present and can't open it until you're finished doing your chores, it's amazing how quickly the work gets done.

"Did you vacuum under there?" Ethan asked as Emily crouched down to peer into the darkness under the bed.

"She will," Mrs. Tuttle said. "Make sure you've also scrubbed the bathroom counters."

Ethan didn't take much longer to finish. He dried the counter, polished the mirror, and put the rag into the hamper. He and Emily came into the hallway at the same time and raced to the kitchen. Mrs. Tuttle stood aside to let them tear into their packages.

"Coats?" Ethan said.

"Well, yours is, but I'm not sure what mine is yet," Emily said. Behind the ripped paper was some light brown material, sewed with wide stitches and embroidered with a pattern she didn't know. It smelled like woodland, like trees and leaves—definitely leather.

Ethan's couldn't have been more different. He pulled out of the ruins of his packaging a scarlet coat with brass buttons. It was longer than a regular coat, with tails in the back that fell to his knees. But it was pretty close to the right size, and made him feel like someone very important. "Look at this... I'm a British soldier!"

"You're a Redcoat!" Emily said. "But I'm not quite sure what I am. Native, for sure, but what kind? There are hundreds of native tribes." There was a buckskin shirt with fringes, and tucked away in the bottom of the package was a pair of soft moccasins—Emily's exact size.

"Go try those on," their mom said. "And I believe you have notes as well." She held up a pair of small cards with writing on them.

The twins snatched at them. They were invitations to meet Fred in his backyard that afternoon, dressed in their new clothing.

"Awesome!" Ethan excitedly said. "Another story about history!"

"Fred said we were going to study the first world war," Emily said. "This doesn't look like the right clothing for that."

"It's a mystery," Ethan said. "Fred likes those. It's a good thing we do, too!"

That afternoon, right on time, the twins arrived at Fred's house. Even though

Fred only lived next door, the twins still attracted attention from neighbors while running across their front lawn dressed as a British soldier and a Native American. They found Fred in his backyard, where he, too, was wearing new clothing. His coat, though, was blue with gold buttons. Fred heard the twins approach, but was busy looking through the lens of a peculiar instrument on a tripod.

"Fred, what's that?" Ethan asked. "Are you spying on our yard?"

"*Je m'appelle Jumonville. Qui est voux?*" Fred said.

The twins looked at each other. Emily shrugged. "I think he's asking your name."

Ethan drew himself up tall. "I am Sir Ethan of Tuttle," he said. "My king demands to know why you are looking at his majesty's land with that doohickey?"

Fred tried not to smile, but it was impossible. His grin split his face. "Well, if England's king so demands.... Using my survey equipment, I've discovered a slight discrepancy with your fence line in relation to my property."

"What do you mean?" Emily replied.

"You're actually intruding on *my* land!" Fred said, as he drew a sword from his side. "In the name of King Louis XV of France, I demand that *you* take your very red coat and that fence back 3 feet!"

"That fence was here when my mom and dad bought this house, so there's no way we're going to move it now!"

Emily stepped between them, her palms out, pushing them apart. "Before you two get too excited—and is that sword real?—let me remind you that *both* of you are on *my* land. Natives were here thousands of years before your people even dreamed it existed."

For a moment, they all stood there, looking defiant. Then they all burst out laughing together.

"Well," Fred said, once he could get his breath, "that's about all for the lesson today. You both seem to have a pretty good handle on the issues that led to the French and Indian War."

"French and Indian War?" Ethan began strutting around the yard, looking at Fred's amazing garden, which was just starting to produce tiny vegetables on the stems and vines of each plant. "Last time, you said something about the first world war."

"True," Fred said. "But before talking about a bitter war, let's sweeten things up with some lemonade. Come with me."

The three of them marched single-file around a tall vine with bean pods beginning to grow. Behind it, on a little cement patio in the shade, were three chairs around a small table. On the table was a tall pitcher of lemonade with three glasses standing around it like a regiment of soldiers waiting for orders.

Fred poured the lemonade and then showed them a map of the world. The map showed areas of land separated in blues, greens, yellows, and reds.

Ethan liked maps. He bent over it. Then his face grew puzzled. "This doesn't look quite right. Shouldn't there be more countries here?" he asked, pointing to eastern Europe.

"Plus, no America," Emily said. "The land is there, but there's no country."

"You're both correct," Fred said. "We're going to zoom out to see what the whole world was like back in the mid-1700s."

"That's almost 150 years after the first colonists came to America," Emily said.

Ethan did some mental math, squinting his eyes shut in concentration. "And about 60 years after the Glorious Revolution of 1688."

"Back then, countries didn't keep their borders where they were," Fred explained. "Many of them were constantly at war, working toward world domination. They wanted to control as much land and resources as possible under one empire. That's called empire building—also known as *colonialism*."

"Even if there were already other people living in those places?" Ethan remarked. "That sounds a lot like stealing."

Emily thought of a space movie they had seen before. The bad guys were called the empire, and that's exactly what they did. They took control of all the planets and battled with anyone who stood in their way.

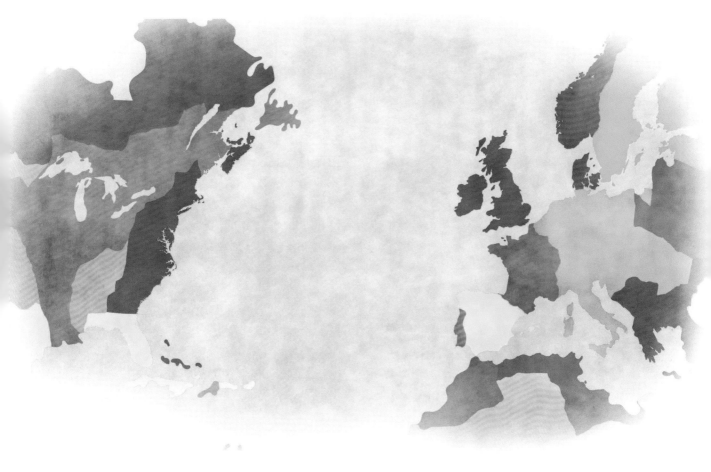

"It seems like Europe was always at war back then," Ethan said. "But these countries get along pretty well today. What changed?"

Fred leaned back and put his finger in the air. "Let's imagine that people in the United States need lumber from trees in Canada or avocados from Mexico. Should we go to war with them and take those things?"

"What? No way!" Emily said. "We can just trade with them. You really don't even need our government to do it, just American customers buying wood from Canadian mills, or Mexican guacamole for our nachos." She licked her lips.

"War would be the worst way to get those things," Ethan agreed. "But something tells me that's exactly what these countries did to each other."

"Some of the smaller countries, like Italy and Holland, did start to figure out that if you offer other countries helpful products, most of them will trade with you and even become friends. But some just couldn't let go of the old ways of war and empire building... especially France and England!"

Fred continued, "Because Britain had a very large and skilled navy, they were able to colonize many places around the world: in Africa, Asia, India, Australia, and they had the most forces in America. The phrase was, 'The sun never sets on the British Empire,' which means they had colonies in so many parts of the world that somewhere, the sun was always shining on one of their conquered lands."

"I don't get it," Ethan said. "If free trade is a more peaceful way to get the things you need for your country, why did they keep empire building?"

"I think there are a few reasons. Why do you think?" Fred asked.

The twins sat for a moment, thinking about what it must have been like to be a king of an empire in the mid 1700s.

"I suppose it's easier for people with power to steal than to pay for something," Ethan offered, "especially if you have obedient navies and armies to do your dirty work."

"Maybe they didn't know any better?" Emily wondered. "Kings still thought they had absolute power, so maybe they thought they could go around bossing everyone. They only understood force and control, and not how to cooperate."

"I think you're both right," Fred said. "I think there might have also been a fear that if you stopped pushing against the other empires, the other empires would push harder against you."

Trade &
Cooperation

Empire &
Colonization

"And then *your* country would be taken over!" Emily said. "Except, look at us, standing here now." She waved her hand over her clothes. "I'm a Native American. You're French—and you're British, Ethan. We're all in the same country, with more than enough space for all of us. But we're still going to fight over it, aren't we?"

Fred frowned. "Yes, Emily. We are. And that brings us into our story—the beginning of that fight that few people know about, even people who think they know a lot about American history."

The Ohio Land Speculators

"Story time!" Ethan said. "I knew it."

Fred started, "Many of the stories of history can be sad—war, slavery, and suffering! It makes you wish you could go back in time and change things."

"Like how the Catholics and Protestants kept killing each other, just because they believed different things about the Bible," Ethan said. "And how governments did empire building instead of trading peacefully."

"Yes," Fred agreed. "But the hard truth is, the sadness from these stories is what teaches us. The lessons learned are why the world can become a much better place than it ever was! If we remember the lessons and continue to learn more,

we'll find that the ending of these sad stories are often happy ones. Will you try to remember that?"

The twins both nodded, intrigued by what they were about to learn. Ethan and Emily settled back into their chairs, their eyes never leaving the storyteller as he began his tale.

"This is a story of a young man, a redcoat officer, only 22 years old, who started a small battle that would bring the whole world to war... and change the world forever. That young man was George Washington."

"Wait, George Washington was a redcoat?" Emily's jaw dropped.

"And he started the French and Indian War... the world war you mentioned?" Ethan's breathing was already growing short by the stress of this thought. "But... why?!"

"We have to go back to when George was a boy, almost exactly your age," Fred said. "He wasn't always the most popular son in the Washington family. That would be his older brother Lawrence, who was twelve years older than he was—already a grown up! Their dad died when George was eleven, so Lawrence acted like a father to him. George loved him a lot."

"Lawrence was also becoming well-known in Virginia. He had built a good business speculating on land."

Emily squinted, trying to remember. "Speculating... that means..."

"Guessing?" Ethan said, guessing himself.

"Pretty close," Fred said, tapping the scabbard of his sword as he talked. "Guessing about the future value of something is what you do when you speculate. You acquire a thing when it's not worth a lot of money, hold onto it, hoping that it will grow in value, so when you finally sell it you'll make extra money."

"So it's like investing," Emily said confidently.

"Exactly. Lawrence was part of a group of land speculators called the Ohio Company that asked the king to grant them land in the Ohio River Valley—which is right here." Fred stood and rolled up a tarp that was covering a large chalk drawing he had made on the patio—a map of colonial America.

"You'll see that the Ohio territory is outside and west of the borders of the colonies," Fred pointed out. "Some of the land was granted to Virginian companies and some to Pennsylvanian companies. But, also, there was some granted to British-owned companies."

More About Us!

Thomas Lee
1690 – 1750

In 1747, Lee founded the Ohio Company of Virginia, a land speculation investment firm which helped colonize the Ohio River Valley. Lee's influence as a member of the Governor's Council helped lead to its success. Within seven years, they brought one hundred families to the territory.

Lawrence Washington
1718-1752

He and his brother Augustine were founding members of the Ohio Company of Virginia and members of the Virginia colonial legislature, the House of Burgesses. To enable ships to port on the Potomac River, for the development of the Ohio territory, Lawrence founded the town of Alexandria on its banks in 1749.

Robert Dinwiddie
1692 – 1770

A British colonial administrator who became lieutenant governor of colonial Virginia, Dinwiddie wanted to limit French expansion in the Ohio territory, an area being settled by the Virginia Ohio Company, of which he was a stockholder. He sent young George Washington to drive off the French.

"But the big problem was that the empire of France claimed the same land."

"Hey, don't forget about the native tribes who had been living there for a long time," Emily said. "All those people claiming the land is theirs... that's not likely to end well."

Fred nodded. "Now, George Washington was often ill as a child. His mother believed that the mountain air would do him good, so when George was a teenager, she got him work with a surveying company, making maps of western Virginia and the Ohio territory."

"Now he had something in common with his big brother. I bet that was fun for him," Ethan said.

"He hiked many miles a day, quickly becoming a healthy, strong, and tall man, and a very skilled land surveyor," Fred said. "He loved surveying so much that he continued surveying land his entire life, even after he was president. But early on, the Washington family believed the Ohio River Valley was going to be part of the colonies; so claiming it, and selling it to the new settlers, would make them very wealthy."

"What did the Washingtons think of the French claiming the land for themselves?" Ethan inquired.

"That could make their 'speculation' worth a lot less, couldn't it?" Emily said. "Like if it became part of France instead of Virginia?"

"The French started building army forts near the land of the Ohio Company, making them very nervous," Fred said. "If France took that land, they would lose their investments. The French wouldn't pay any attention to their land claims."

More About Us!
Ohio Natives

British colonists had been in violent competition for land with native people for hundreds of years. The French Canadians, however, were mostly in a business partnership with the western tribes of the Ohio River, due to the fur trapping business that enriched them both. When the interests of colonial settlers and the French-Canadian fur industries clashed over those western territories, it was no surprise that most of the tribes allied themselves with French forces. Thanks to the peaceful relationship the Quakers of Pennsylvania had with the Iroquois Confederacy, they largely stayed neutral in the conflict, while some even fought alongside the British colonists.

"Ouch. They'd lose a lot of potential profit," Emily said.

"They would. And as an expert land surveyor, George paid very close attention to all that land. He hoped he and Lawrence would own it for a long time..." Fred paused for a moment, "But then, Lawrence died."

"Poor George," Ethan said.

"Two years later, Virginia's governor, Robert Dinwiddie, who was also a shareholder in the Ohio Land Company, asked young George Washington to lead a troop of soldiers to the Ohio territory to build another fort to make sure the French knew that this land was already claimed. George knew the area well, and that knowledge would help keep the French out. This journey began a series

of events that would dramatically change history, though none of them could have known it at the time."

"George's first mission into the Ohio wilderness was not successful," Fred continued. "He identified a good site for a fort but the French army was already in the area. Washington told the French that the land was claimed by Virginia and by the Ohio Company, and gave them written orders to leave. Of course, the French refused."

"Why am I not surprised?" Emily said.

Fred smiled. "Being outnumbered, Washington and his troops had little choice but to return to Governor Dinwiddie and report that they were unsuccessful in building a fort. But the cunning George had been observing the positions and numbers of the French army the whole time."

"Gathering military intelligence!" Ethan said.

"Kind of like a spy!" Emily added.

"George suggested that the French could be driven off if he only had more men," Fred explained. "His written reports were published and became very popular reading material in the colonies. The reports even went to London, where the British also loved reading about this tall, dashing young officer who was exploring the frontier of America."

"They really read his letters in *London*?" Ethan asked. "They must have been desperate for news because that sounds a little boring."

"Not to them," Emily said. "America was like... I don't know... the moon. I remember hearing about the first moon landing—everyone who had a television watched it. It was the most important thing in the world. I bet this wasn't so different from that."

Fred nodded. "Just like it did for Neil Armstrong, reports from the frontier made Washington popular. The Governor promoted Washington to Lieutenant Colonel and gave him permission to raise an army and drive out the French. This didn't go well—few men were willing to leave their homes, march into the wilderness, and risk being killed. Why would they? They wouldn't get paid very much. It wasn't *their* land they were defending."

This Washington fellow is quite a strapping lad. Don't you think, Daughter?

George Starts a World War

"That makes sense," Ethan said. "On the other hand, people like Washington and his family who speculated on the land wanted to fight for it."

"But random people from the colonies who weren't invested in it?" Emily added. "No way. I wouldn't do it."

Fred continued: "Few colonists volunteered and the different colonial assemblies didn't want to fund it by taxes either, but Washington got word of a native tribe that was willing to fight alongside the colonial troops. This gave him enough men to start the fight, hoping that others would join."

He drew a line from Virginia to Ohio. "It might have worked too... but the French were aware the Americans were marching their way, and sent 50 soldiers to protect the area Washington wanted—a valley about where Pittsburgh, Pennsylvania is today. The French arrived first and set up a small fort." Fred finished drawing the line and made an X on the map.

He took off his coat and hung it on the back of his chair. "Washington and the native warriors planned to surround the camp and force the French to leave."

Fred lowered his head and squinted his eyes, looking back and forth. He beckoned the twins into the thick brush of the garden and crouched low, peering through the

More About This!

JOIN, or DIE.

The Albany Plan of Union
July 10, 1754 – Albany, New York

Representatives of several northern colonies gathered in response to the French and Indian War, spurred on by George Washington's actions in the Ohio Valley.

A plan was proposed by a Pennsylvanian delegate, Benjamin Franklin, that the colonies would form a central government, with a president and colonial assembly, to impose taxes and raise an army. Franklin created a drawing of a snake to symbolize the potential defensive power of the united colonies. The delegates agreed to the plan, but when it was presented to the local colonial assemblies and to the British, it was rejected.

Franklin observed, "The colonial assemblies and most of the people were narrowly provincial in outlook, mutually jealous, and suspicious of any central taxing authority." The colonists were wisely cautious about a new taxing power. The idea threatened the local governments that they had enjoyed since the Mayflower Compact.

The English also rejected the plan, as they feared a union of colonies would be a threat to their own influence and power over them.

Though the plan failed, it opened a door for future collaboration between the colonies.

bushes, as if stalking something... or someone. He put his finger to his lips and pulled the twins down beside him. His voice came as a whisper.

"There. That's the French camp." He pointed to the table where his blue French coat now dangled from one of the chairs. "We caught the French sleeping. Their commander is a man named Jumonville, and we've got them surrounded." Slowly, Fred drew his sword and pointed it at the "camp."

Ethan held his breath. His heart hammered. Was this what it was like? What if there were men there in the clearing? What if they woke up? What if they shot back?

Fred sprang to his feet and called out, "Let them have it, men!"

Emily and Ethan couldn't help themselves. They jumped up and charged. There was no one there, of course, but Ethan did capture a glass of lemonade.

Suddenly, a loud bang rang out that startled the twins. Ethan thought he may have even screamed a little, and judging by the way Emily was now looking at him, he sensed that must be correct.

Fred revealed his musket—a toy pop gun, but a loud one. "To this day, no one knows for sure which side fired first—though Washington always took responsibility for telling his men to fire, and may have himself fired the first shot!—but the Americans, having a much better position, fired most effectively, killing a few of the Frenchmen. The French were forced to surrender."

"I know we've already talked about a lot of war and killing in our lessons, but this part makes me sad," Ethan said.

"Yeah, I don't like to hear about George Washington killing people. I wish they had better understood free trade and cooperation instead of empire building back then," Emily added.

"Well, something even more terrible happened next," Fred pressed on. "The native leader—his name was Half-King—was only using the Americans so he could get revenge on the French. Even though the French had already surrendered, Half-King and his warriors killed Commander Jumonville and other Frenchmen with their tomahawks before Washington could stop them. One Frenchman escaped and returned to his base, which wasn't far away. He told the story and blamed Washington for everything that had happened."

Ethan said, "Oh no! That's awful!"

"The French were obviously furious," Fred added, putting his coat back on. "You would be, too—right? And Washington knew they would come for revenge, so he retreated his men to a meadow southward and built a fort they called Fort Necessity. As suspected, the French followed, and surrounded the fort. After a short battle, the colonists had to surrender. It was the only time Washington ever had to surrender in all the battles he fought. Although Washington wasn't hurt, he was forced to sign a document that said Commander Jumonville was assassinated—killed without a chance to surrender."

Emily said, "Why would he sign? It's not exactly what happened. It was Half-King!"

"Well, the document was in French, and Washington couldn't read it," Fred replied. "He probably didn't understand what he was admitting to. Either way, the document was sent to France, where they called it an act of war and a massacre—and blamed Washington for starting it. Before long, the French and the English were calling up thousands of their troops to fight. The French formed an alliance with the native tribes in the Ohio Valley, and war was declared."

"There's the world war," Emily said.

"All because of a fight over some land for the Ohio Company," Ethan said. "The French had plenty of reasons to be mad. What happened to Commander Jumonville and his men was really awful."

Fred nodded somberly. "The anger sparked fighting back in Europe too. There, the French allied with the Russians and the Spanish. The English allied with the Portuguese and the Prussians. The war raged all over the planet. There was fighting on every continent except Antarctica—but that was probably because nobody knew it was there yet. And with that, the Seven Years' War had begun."

The Tory's Grand Design

Emily stared at Fred's chalk map, thinking. "It's weird thinking about George Washington as a redcoat. The British even loved him. He was a war hero to them. That's going to make the next part of the story extra weird, isn't it? Washington eventually becoming the colonial commander and all. Like one of your best friends showing up to play for the other team."

"Yeah, but the British won, right?" Ethan said. "I'm only asking because this red coat is so cool."

"As far as how the world war turned out, it wasn't as clear-cut as that," Fred said, "but as far as the war in America was concerned, yes, the British were successful in pushing the French back over the Mississippi River."

"Ha!" Ethan said. "I knew it." He punched his fist in the air.

"Not so fast, Ethan." Fred put black chalk to the map, drawing a long, thick line between the British colonies and the new land that they won from the French. "This is the Proclamation Line of 1763. Part of the treaty that ended the war was a promise that the colonists wouldn't settle any more lands between the Mississippi River and the Appalachian Mountains right here."

"Really?" Ethan said. "That's right where the colonial speculators were claiming the new land as their own!"

"It's actually *my* land," Emily said. "The native tribes!"

"But you lost!" Ethan said. He scrunched up his face, thinking. "Why would the British agree to give up the thing the colonists were fighting for in the first place? They won, after all!"

Emily thought hard, too, while Fred started gathering their costumes. "Well... did the colonists win or did the British win? Maybe the colonists *thought* the British were fighting for them, but really they were fighting for... something else."

Fred smiled, watching them think. "You're exactly right. King George II and the Whigs in Parliament let the American colonists mostly govern themselves, as did most of the kings before them."

"But," he said poignantly, "during the last battles of the Seven Years' War, King George II died, leaving the throne to his grandson, King George III. He was a very different king. He favored another group in Parliament called the Tories. They had a new plan, a 'Grand Design' for the colonies... and the Americans were about to find out what it was."

"Please don't tell us this is the end of the lesson!" Emily pleaded. "What was the plan?"

"I'll just tell you this," Fred smiled. "The British spent so much money on seven

years of war, and they wanted to get some of it back. This area here, that was now off limits to settlers, was preserved for the fur trade. Companies in London could make a lot of money from American beaver fur."

"That's a real bummer for colonial land speculators," Ethan observed.

"What about the other colonists?" Emily said. "They probably didn't care so much about the loss of the land. What was the new plan for them?"

More About Me!

King George III
1738-1820

George III took the throne after the death of his grandfather, George II. He favored Tory ministers in the government, upsetting the Whigs who saw him as an autocrat.

Lord North and the new Tory-controlled Parliament began tightening up the enforcement of taxes in Britain and the Americas, igniting a revolt that would eventually lead to war and George's loss of the colonies.

His mind was no doubt deeply affected by this assault on his pride; toward the end of his life, he was often heard arguing with an imaginary Lord North and was called "Mad King George."

"Keeping the colonists closer to the coastline had another benefit." He put his hand on Ethan's shoulder. "Can you guess?"

Ethan snapped his fingers. He knew the answer. "Control! It's too hard to tax people who want to live free on the frontier. Keep them near the shore where they could be forced to obey them."

"Correct. And the new king and Tory Parliament were preparing thousands of troops to make sure the colonists followed the new plan, paid their taxes, and played by their rules. So how does that make you feel?" Fred asked.

Emily frowned. "They're taking advantage of us. They made us fight in a war that most of us didn't want in the first place. All they care about is using us to make money. We're just pawns in their game—pawns for their empire."

"Okay, I sense things are starting to fall in place," Ethan said. "George Washington's war didn't just change history because it started a world war. That war started something bigger."

Fred put his hand behind his ear. "Sounds like someone's beating the drum of revolution."

A Thought From Connor

How do you think history might have unfolded had George Washington and others not started the French and Indian War?

I've heard some people suggest that we wouldn't have the country we now do, or its Constitution, had these early events not happened. But do we know that for sure? For all we know, our world today would be much better had these early wars and conflicts not occurred.

It's impossible to say. What I do think is important is that we not justify bad things in the past because good things came about because of them. The ends don't justify the means—in other words, we should always do what's right, even if there might be some positive results from doing things the wrong way.

Let's Talk About It!

When empires choose to clash over resources or disagreements of any kind, their actions involve and impact many innocent people who have nothing to do with the competing interests of those governments. Most regular people want to trade and live in harmony with others, yet their lives are disrupted by the destructive ambitions of those in power.

When wars break out in our day, innocent people are inevitably impacted in negative ways. History is full of such examples.

Knowing this, how can we evaluate when a war is necessary? Is it okay to tolerate the loss of innocent life to achieve a desired outcome? If so, what are the circumstances that have to exist in order to justify it?

Chapter 6
In the King's Grip

Liberals and Conservatives

Emily munched her popcorn, sitting lazily on the couch while she watched TV. The camera showed a man on one side of a tall stage and a woman on the other. They each stood behind wooden podiums with eagles on them. They argued with each other while another woman—the moderator—tried to keep them focused on the questions she was asking.

Ethan sat at the other end of the couch. He had a notebook perched on his legs. He hadn't written much, but had eaten most of his bag of sour gummy fish.

"So, what have you written down so far?" Emily asked.

"The woman is Jan Jennings, and she's a... conservative," Ethan said, scanning his notes. "The man is Robert Dunworth, and he's... well, I don't know. She calls him a terrorist, but he calls himself a 'liberal,' whatever that is."

"That's all you've written?" Emily asked. "We've been watching for twenty minutes."

"Well, they're not making a lot of sense. I keep hoping they'll actually answer the questions, but they seem more interested in calling each other names."

Their dad walked through the room and paused when he saw the TV. "Dad, what's a 'liberal'?" Ethan asked.

Mr. Tuttle sat on an arm of the sofa. "Where did you hear that term?"

Ethan pointed at the TV.

"I better take a chair," their dad said. "This might take a minute." He sank down into the loveseat. Emily aimed the remote at the TV and turned it down. "Okay. We can start with the basic terms," Mr. Tuttle said. "First, I bet she said she was a 'conservative,' didn't she? What do you think that word means?"

"It sounds like the word *conserve*, which means to protect something or keep it from running out," Ethan said.

"Right. That's where the word came from—the people who wanted to 'conserve' the laws and systems that we already have often call themselves conservatives. Initially, they were known for caution, not making hasty decisions, and more likely to vote against new things," Mr. Tuttle explained. "Now, what do you think 'liberal' means?" He looked over at Emily.

She shrugged. "The conservative lady, Jan Jennings, says liberals are like socialists."

"Words are funny things," Mr. Tuttle said, reaching out to get some popcorn for himself. "Once upon a time, *liberal* had a very different meaning. Can you think of words that sound like it?"

Ethan said, "Liberty! Maybe even, I don't know, library?"

"All those words come from another Latin word," Mr. Tuttle said. "*Liber* means 'free.' A liberal used to be a person who believed in freedom of choice, allowing people to make their own decisions."

"So library books make us free?" Ethan said. "Sounds right to me!"

More About Us!

Tories / Conservatives
Royalists - Cavaliers

Their philosophy came from the Cavaliers—the Royalists during the English Civil War. They fought to conserve the absolute authority of the monarchy and the Anglican Church.

The word *Tory* was an insult derived from the Irish language meaning "a cruel robber."

Once the liberals started using the insulting word *Whig* as a badge of honor, and even naming their political party after it, the conservatives started calling themselves Tories in response.

After a period of Whig control of the government during King George II's reign, the Tories would take control under George III and press the colonies to submit to their authority.

Whigs / Liberals
Parliamentarians - Roundheads

When Scottish country folk would drive their cattle down the street, they'd call out "Chuig." With their accent, it sounded like "Whig" to the English, who started calling them "Whiggamores."

Later, it was largely the Scottish who revolted against the King in the Civil War, so the term was used as a slur to describe anyone who opposed the absolute power of the King and the Anglican Church. It was these people who became inspired by the ideas of liberalism—human rights, democracy, and limited government.

These ideas were eventually codified in the English Bill of Rights and the American Declaration of Independence.

"Knowledge can make us free, yes," Mr. Tuttle replied.

"So in the old days, a liberal was someone who believed in liberty?" Emily asked. By now, she'd lost interest in the debate.

"That's a pretty good definition," Mr. Tuttle said. "In colonial times, a liberal was called a Whig—someone who probably read John Locke. They wanted to create a new system of government that protected human rights. A conservative was called a Tory. They wanted to conserve the British system of government—mercantilism and the succession of kings."

Ethan thought about what they'd been learning with Fred. "Which colonists were liberal Whigs and which were conservative Tories? So far in our stories with Fred most of the colonists seem like they were loyal to the King."

"Nice observation," Mr. Tuttle nodded, chewing popcorn. Salty, not too buttery—just the way he liked it. "For the most part, the colonists were fine being British citizens."

"But then something happened that made them question whether the British government accepted them as citizens."

Emily sat up. "We know about this! King George III and Parliament sent thousands of redcoat soldiers to force the colonists to pay taxes and stop their trade with other countries!"

"Fred really is teaching you well. That disrespectful action turned many loyal conservatives into radical liberals, but no one was really talking about independence yet. They just wanted to have their rights respected, just like other British subjects," he said. The popcorn was making Mr. Tuttle thirsty. He looked around for a drink.

"Tell you what, Dad," Ethan said. "If you'll tell us about these liberals and conservatives so we can impress Fred when we meet again, I'll go get us all some root beer from the fridge."

Mr. Tuttle accepted the deal. He took a book from the bookshelf, Ethan got three bottles of fizzy root beer, and Emily refilled the bowl of popcorn. Then they settled back down for the story.

The Iron Fist

"First," Mr. Tuttle began, "since you know about the French and Indian War, you should know that the British spent a lot of money on that war."

"It wasn't just in America," Emily said. "Fred said it was a world war. That must have cost a lot."

"It did." He twisted off the cap of his root beer and took a long drink. "King George III and the Tories ruled with an iron fist. They thought that since they'd spent so much money protecting the colonies, that it was time that the colonists started paying their share of taxes, too."

Emily frowned and shook her head. "But they didn't really care about protecting the colonists, Dad. Most of the Americans didn't even want to fight in the war in the first place."

"What the colonists wanted didn't matter much," he shrugged. "They were subjects to the King and had to do what he said." Mr. Tuttle reached out and picked up Ethan's root beer. He took a swig from it. Ethan stared at him with his mouth open. Mr. Tuttle smiled back. "Dad taxes. You're my subject."

Emily reached out and snatched up her bottle of root beer before her dad could also "tax" her. "That reminds me! Fred taught us that the British sent redcoats over to stop the free trading and to collect taxes, but also to stop the colonists from moving to the frontier... which is why I'm putting my root beer over here behind the lamp where you can't get it!"

Mr. Tuttle laughed. "That's exactly what happened. For more than a hundred years, the American colonists were mostly left alone to discover freedom for themselves. They lived in a rich land of opportunity. They became industrious, wealthy, independent, and locally governed by assemblies. They were happy and healthy. They were British subjects on paper, but, in reality, they were already independent and free. And the Whig Parliament didn't care to enforce the rules too strictly."

Ethan returned his root beer to its rightful place in front of him. "We usually think that Americans became free after the Revolution, but you're right... because they lived so far away, and because Great Britain was dealing with their own problems all that time, they were already basically free. And I bet they liked it."

"Now imagine that distant government, now under Tory control, coming to make you pay more taxes, forcing you to fight in its wars, telling you who you couldn't trade with, and where you couldn't live," he added. "Many of the colonists chose to disobey."

"How *did* they get away with it?" Emily asked.

More About This!

Salutary Neglect

After the Glorious Revolution, Whigs were in control. Their unofficial policy was to relax the enforcement of trade laws imposed on the American colonies and focus attention on more important matters in Europe.

Edmund Burke, a Whig, said this "wise and salutary neglect" was the prime factor in the booming commercial success of the colonies. It enabled the American colonies to prosper by trading with non-British entities, and then spend that wealth on British-made goods, while at the same time providing Britain with raw materials for manufacture.

The Grand Design

The new Tory-controlled Parliament saw that salutary neglect enabled the colonies to become economically and politically independent, which cut into mercantilist profits and reduced the tax revenue needed to pay for the king's wars.

Their plan was to start enforcing trade laws and institute direct taxes that bypassed colonial legislatures. The excuse for these new policies was to pay for the arrival of British troops to protect the newly won Ohio Territory. But the truth was soon realized—the troops were, in fact, sent to stop settlers from encroaching on the land that was used for lucrative English beaver fur companies and to bring the colonies back under control!

Mr. Tuttle grabbed another handful of popcorn. "These stories are quite amazing... and even funny. The free traders (whom the British called smugglers) would make friends with the tax collectors. When they came into port with their ships full of smuggled Dutch tea or Caribbean molasses, the tax collector would say, 'You owe six pounds for the King!', but the smugglers would wink back at them and say, 'Hey, friend, how about I give two pounds to you, and you pretend you never saw my ship?'"

"Madness... a conspiracy!" Ethan said, using his best British accent.

"That worked most of the time, but sometimes they'd get caught by the Royal Navy red-handed!" Mr. Tuttle pointed to Emily's hidden root beer.

"Poor smugglers," Emily said, guarding her bottle. "There's no way out of that!"

"You'd think so, wouldn't you?" Mr. Tuttle said. "But the redcoats would drag them to court and present their evidence to the judge and jury. And because the jury was made up of the smugglers' friends and neighbors who enjoyed the smuggled goods themselves, they would say *not guilty*!"

"What?!" Emily said in amazement. "Can you imagine how mad those redcoats must have been?"

"Sounds like Americans were rascals," Ethan said, with a big smile. "Or... radicals."

"The Tories couldn't let them get away with it," Mr. Tuttle continued. "They replaced all the local tax collectors, and took control of their courts. This was an attack on everything they ever knew."

"So it wasn't just the taxes that upset them," Ethan sighed. "It was like an attack on everything that had made them free."

"And Parliament also passed a series of new laws to try to get the colonists under control... to show them who was boss!"

He opened the book he had been holding and showed a page with a long list of taxes: The Navigation Acts, the Sugar Act, and the Currency Act. "These taxes were different from the other taxes, and they made the colonists very upset."

"How were these taxes different? Did they have to pay more?" Ethan asked.

"In some cases the taxes were less," Mr. Tuttle answered. "But this time, the taxes were controlled by the British Parliament and not the colonist's local assemblies. They were being taxed without having a vote in the matter."

"No taxation without representation!" Ethan said. "That's what the colonists used to say."

Mr. Tuttle pointed back to the book. "Taxes without representation—that's why these attempts to tax the colonists made them more angry than before. But still, they didn't want to stand up against their government... even many of the liberals wouldn't. They were still loyal to the King and many of them even sided with the Tories... especially this guy."

He took from his wallet a $100 bill and laid it on the coffee table. "Benjamin Franklin," Mr. Tuttle said. "He seemed to welcomed the troops and criticized people for complaining about the taxes. In fact, some of these policies may have been *his* ideas."

"What? I can't believe it. He's supposed to be a hero of the Revolution!" Ethan said, reaching for the money.

"Not yet, he wasn't." Mr. Tuttle said. "Franklin spent much of his life living in London working with Parliament and the King's team. When colonial leaders saw that these new taxes were upsetting the people, they sent Franklin back to London to help figure out new ways to tax the colonies—ways that wouldn't make them so upset."

Mr. Tuttle grabbed the bill and put it back in his wallet. "But it didn't work— it actually got worse... *much* worse. Parliament hatched a sneaky plan." Mr. Tuttle flipped to the next chapter of the book and showed them an image of an old newspaper with the words *Pennsylvania Gazette* at the top. A stamp blocked out part of the writing. Their dad pointed to it. "What's this?"

"A postage stamp?" Ethan guessed.

"It looks like one, yes," he replied, "and it's somewhat similar. To mail a letter, you need a postage stamp, right?"

The twins nodded. Mr. Tuttle continued: "Parliament passed a new law that said *any* printed material—newspapers, legal documents, even playing cards—had to have a stamp on it that people would have to purchase; otherwise, it would be illegal. It was called—"

"The Stamp Act!" Emily said. "Those stamps were sold by the British government. That was how they were going to get money from them without really taxing them. What a sneaky trick.... Boy, that would have made me so angry! I couldn't even put up a lost pet flyer without paying the British for it!"

"What about Benjamin Franklin?" Ethan asked. "He was in London. Did he try to stop it?"

"It's hard to know what he tried, but after the Stamp Act was passed, he got his friends and relatives jobs as stamp masters. He also encouraged the colonial newspapers to write articles supporting it."

Ethan put both of his hands over his face, "Oh, Ben, how could you?"

"I guess I don't blame him. I mean, how could he really fight back?" Emily said. "The government sent so many redcoats to make them obey. It couldn't be stopped."

"You would think that, but you'd be wrong," Mr. Tuttle said. "Do you know the saying, 'The pen is mightier than the sword'? What do you think that means?"

More About This!
Stamp Act of 1765

This Act of the British Parliament imposed another direct tax on the American colonists, but in a way that was more difficult for them to avoid paying.

This time it required that printed materials, including legal documents, playing cards, newspapers, and many other things, be produced on paper embossed with a special stamp to prove the British tax had been paid in British currency, not in colonial paper money.

The Stamp Act was so unpopular among colonists that it led them to openly protest. The public outcry forced colonial assemblies to respond with resolutions and declarations officially rejecting the Stamp Act.

"It means that sharing ideas can be powerful enough to change people's minds," Ethan said.

"Meanwhile, violence probably doesn't change people's minds," Emily added.

"I'm so proud of you two," Mr. Tuttle beamed. "Only the most radical liberals were brave enough to speak up in their colonial assemblies, like Samuel Adams, James Otis, and Patrick Henry. They gave great speeches and proposed radical resolutions for debate—ones that clearly communicated the liberal ideas that John Locke wrote about, such as consent of the governed, the rights of the people, and representative government."

"These ideas spread quickly through the colonies and convinced the people that is was time to take a stand—not just with resolutions on paper from their political assemblies, but a real resistance to Parliament and the Stamp Act."

Mr. Tuttle sat forward. "Next, the hard part. How can you actually fight back? The Tory governors and thousands of armed redcoats aren't going to let you disobey the laws!"

He gathered up the empty root beer bottles. "You two think about that while I take these to the trash." He got up and left for the kitchen, leaving the twins to think.

The Sons Are Born

Ethan laid back on the cushions and lowered his voice to a whisper. "The local assemblies are starting to speak out against the Stamp Act, but if we're going to actually stand up to the British, we have to make a plan and act together—we need to have a meeting."

"But if we hold a meeting to organize a revolt, we'll be arrested for treason," Emily whispered in reply. "We're standing against the most powerful government in the world."

Ethan ran his hand through his hair. "Yeah. Not being able to meet openly really limits our options, so we'll have to do it where the British can't hear us. We need—"

"A secret club!" Emily said.

Mr. Tuttle came back in. "What secret club?"

The twins looked around the room, avoiding looking their dad in the eye. "I don't know what you mean," Emily said. "No secret club here..."

"Sneaky," said Mr. Tuttle, and they all laughed. "But you got it, actually. The colonists didn't want to pay those taxes until they had representation in how they were taxed. So a group of Boston

More About This!

Rights of the British Colonies

James Otis,
Massachusetts

James Otis was a legislator from Boston. In his 1764 response to the Revenue Act, he wrote that when rights are violated by the government, the government should be overthrown. About the issue of direct taxes imposed by Parliament, he wrote, "Taxation without representation is tyranny." This soon became the slogan widely used by tax protesters.

The Virginia Resolves

Patrick Henry,
Virginia

In 1765, as a newly elected Virginia legislator, Patrick Henry presented seven resolutions against the Stamp Act. Only four ultimately passed, while the last three were rejected due to their treasonous ideas.

Still, news across the colonies reported that all seven passed! This inaccurate news encouraged radicals across the colonies to prepare for open rebellion.

merchants, along with Samuel Adams and John Hancock, partnered with some local troublemakers. They organized in taverns and agreed to fight against the Stamp Act. They called themselves the Sons of Liberty."

"Because the Stamp Act was so unpopular, many more people joined the secret club. The Sons of Liberty grew rapidly. Within a few months, other Sons of Liberty groups were formed in the other colonies. Their first plan was a mass boycott of all British imports."

"What's a boycott?" Ethan asked.

"Well, if city ports refused to allow British ships to unload their goods, there wouldn't be any taxes collected. Both the Crown and British mercantilists would lose money. And that's actually what happened. The boycott was a success! The situation was a nightmare for the British, because they could not collect taxes on the goods that were not allowed ashore."

"How did the colonists get by without buying all that stuff they needed?" Emily wondered out loud.

More About Us!

The Sons of Liberty

Every year on November 5th, anti-Catholic gangs in Boston would march through the streets to hang a mannequin of the Pope (called an effigy) on a large elm tree in the middle of town. Inspired by Patrick Henry's Virginia Resolves of 1765 against the Stamp Act, a secret band of Boston businessmen called the Loyal Nine reorganized these groups to protest against the Act. Members started calling themselves the Sons of Liberty. Their new effigy was of the local stamp collector, and the large elm tree was renamed the Liberty Tree. With his life threatened, the local stamp collector quit.

By the end of 1765, Sons of Liberty groups had popped up in each of the colonies and, through pamphlets and leaflets, communicated a unified resistance movement. By boycotting British goods, burning stamp shipments, and threatening anyone participating in the Stamp Act, they were successful in causing every stamp collector to either resign or flee the country.

The Stamp Act Congress

Meanwhile, colonial politicians realized that they had to do something to represent the angry voices of their people. They organized Committees of Correspondence, electing representatives called delegates to meet together in New York to decide what to do. This meeting was called the Stamp Act Congress, which issued a declaration that they would only pay taxes that were properly issued by a government that included their representation and voice.

Between the focused intensity of the Sons of Liberty and the official consensus of an elected Congress, the Stamp Act was never enforced and was repealed.

They had won, but an even more important result was the system of organization that was created. The process of electing delegates to meet with delegates from other colonies would be used ten years later to form the First Continental Congress, which for the first time would informally unify the colonies under the Articles of Association!

The only thing getting stamped today are his hindquarters!

"The women played a critical role; some called them the Daughters of Liberty. They sewed their own clothes and helped each other. But for some things, they just did without. They weren't willing to back down."

"Girl power!" Emily said. "But I'm sure the British didn't back down, either. Did they?"

"Almost," Mr. Tuttle replied. "When the mercantilists in Britain were losing a lot of money, they started complaining to Parliament too!"

"You said *almost*. That means they *didn't* stop," Ethan guessed.

"Nope. The Sons of Liberty had another plan besides the boycotts. As the stamps and stamp masters arrived on ships there were riots throughout the colonies—setting fire to piles of stamps, running British officials out of town, and threatening all the stamp masters to resign or die!"

"Sheesh..." Ethan said, his eyes wide. "Looks like the liberals were a little more serious than the conservatives expected. It's like the revolution already started."

"Pretty close," Mr. Tuttle replied. "Colonists began electing delegates to meet in New York and address what was happening with the protests. It was called the Stamp Act Congress. There they signed an official Declaration of Rights and Grievances to send to Parliament. This was no longer simply the protest of a secret group—it was now official policy. Parliament repealed the Stamp Act. No tax was ever collected."

"It's amazing they were able to push back against the biggest empire in the world, and win!" Ethan said.

"Also, they organized so well across all the colonies, without phones or the internet!" Emily added.

Mr. Tuttle put his arms around his children. "And now, time for us to get to bed. Did I answer your question well enough?"

"Yes... maybe a little more than necessary," Emily said, catching the yawn from her dad. "The colonists are finally starting to act like Americans—like Patriots!"

"I hope Benjamin Franklin ditches those mean Tories and joins them," Ethan said.

Emily looked at the muted TV. She had forgotten it was even on. The "liberal" Robert Dunworth didn't seem to represent liberty like in the old days. And whatever Jan Jennings was trying to conserve didn't seem like liberty, either. She wondered if the ideas of true liberalism would ever be part of American politics again.

A Thought From Elijah

In this chapter, there were two strategies the colonists used to attempt to make change. These strategies seem to be opposites and even contradict each other.

The Tuttles agreed that you can't change someone's mind with violence. Yet, the Sons of Liberty certainly persuaded the tax collectors to change their minds about enforcing the Stamp Act—and they accomplished that with violence and threats... Yikes!

So how do we reconcile the success the Sons of Liberty had using violence with the peaceful approach of writing letters, sending petitions, and pursuing diplomacy?

Let me use an example that may be more familiar to you. Have you ever been forced to take a yucky medicine, eat a food you don't care for, or do a chore that you don't like? Even though you might have ended up doing it to avoid punishment, in the end, the threat of punishment probably didn't make you change your opinion about it. It only forced you to choose between obeying or suffering. The only way to really change your mind is for you to choose to do things on your own. You need to be persuaded!

Now let's go back to the Stamp Act riots. The colonists, through their assemblies, made so many attempts to persuade the British Parliament to change their minds and to give people a say in how they were to be taxed. They would have preferred to use persuasion, but that option became increasingly limited. They didn't have a vote; they didn't have representation. They weren't even respected enough to be heard by the British government.

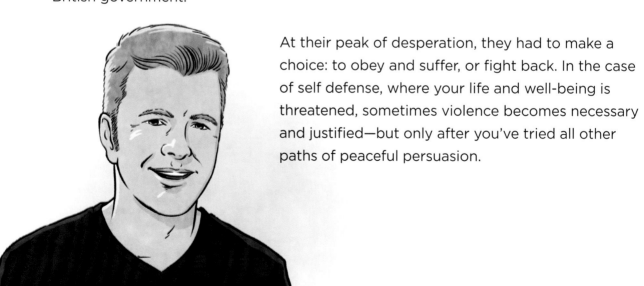

At their peak of desperation, they had to make a choice: to obey and suffer, or fight back. In the case of self defense, where your life and well-being is threatened, sometimes violence becomes necessary and justified—but only after you've tried all other paths of peaceful persuasion.

Let's Talk About It!

If you consider yourself a conservative today, chances are you would have been a liberal in the colonial era—fighting for natural rights and limited government.

Those we consider to be a liberal today would have been called conservative during colonial times—supporting the political establishment and preserving or expanding its power.

That sounds like the exact opposite!

Labels can change meaning over time depending on the people who use them, which can create a lot of confusion. Imagine that a few players on an opposing soccer team suddenly start wearing your team's jersey. Are they really on your team? Should you pass the ball to them? Do they have the same goals that you do?

That's the danger of associating too closely with labels and teams. When we unite ourselves with a particular tribe, if that tribe starts changing, we sometimes become disconnected from the original ideas or principles over time.

In our day, most Americans consider themselves either a conservative or a liberal, but these terms don't convey much about what someone actually believes, since people with widely different beliefs often use the same label. Lots of people wear the same political "jersey" despite pursuing different goals.

What label do you feel best describes *your* beliefs? Do you think other people who use that term would understand what you actually believe? Are there any circumstances in which using that label might cause confusion?

Sour Fish

Emily tapped the plate with her baseball bat and pulled her cap down to block the sun. Ethan took a lead off second base. He dug his cleats into the dirt, getting a good grip for running.

On the mound, the pitcher leaned forward, getting ready to throw.

Emily saw Ethan digging in so she stepped away from the plate and took off her hat, pretending to wipe sweat from her forehead... but this was really a signal to Ethan: *don't try to steal third*. She made sure Ethan could see her. Then she put the hat back on, and stepped into the batter's box again.

Despite Emily's warning, Ethan dug in deeper. He tensed his muscles and waited.

The pitch was a fastball. It was wide of the plate. Emily let it go by, a ball.

Ethan rocketed toward third base.

"He's stealing!" the second baseman yelled.

The catcher had a clear throw to third base, and it was right on the money. Ethan dove like Superman but was tagged out by at least a foot.

The other team erupted in cheers. They'd won the game!

Emily stood at the plate leaning on her bat, defeated. Ethan lay in the dirt, hands outstretched toward third, like he was trying to touch it, but it was just out of reach.

Their team filed onto the field and shook hands with their opponents. "Good game," they all said. They'd had their share of losses, but they were sadder than usual. Emily was their best hitter and could have put them back in the lead. If only she had gotten a chance to hit!

Even after everyone else had gone home, Ethan and Emily still sat on the dugout bench, Ethan at one end, and Emily at the other. Ethan picked dirt out of his cleats. Emily rooted around in her bag, looking for something.

"I could have made it to third," Ethan said.

"But you didn't," Emily said, disgusted. "And I told you not to try it."

Ethan knocked his cleats together. He didn't look at her. "I was sure I could make it."

"But you *didn't*." Her fingers found the thing she was looking for. She drew it out of the bag—a little pouch of gummy fish. The candy had been in there a long time. The pieces of candy wouldn't be good for eating. But they would be hard. That was what she wanted.

She ripped the pouch open and grabbed one of the fish. Like lightning, she whipped it down the dugout and pegged Ethan in the neck.

"Ouch!" he said. "Why did you do that?"

"You saw me," she said angrily. "You watched me take off my cap and put it back on. That's the sign for *don't steal*. You saw it. But you didn't listen. I didn't even get a chance to hit, and that cost us the game."

"You might not have gotten a hit," Ethan said. He looked down at the ground. He knew she probably would have. And then they'd probably have won the game.

Emily didn't answer him. She stormed out, got on her bike, and rode home.

The twins were putting their baseball gear away when their mom came in from the mailbox with a pair of letters. "One for each of you," she said, handing them over.

The twins had become familiar with the envelopes with fancy script on them. "Another lesson with Fred," Emily said, her mood lightening a bit.

Ethan tore into his envelope and drew out a single card with a question: "How can you reason with someone who is being unreasonable?"

"Is this a question or a riddle?" Emily said from across the room. She held up her card. Printed on it was the same question Ethan had read.

"Flip it over," Ethan said. On the back, it read "Lake Ocowoc, East Dock, 6pm, Tuesday."

"That's tomorrow," Emily said. "I guess you only have one day to try to figure out the answer to Fred's question."

"Why do I have to figure it out? What about you?" Ethan said.

"I already know the answer because I have a brother who doesn't listen to reason!" She took her letter and left the room in a huff.

Ethan rubbed at his neck. It didn't hurt anymore, but he could still remember the tiny sting of that sour fish. "Yeah... I get it." He kicked at the carpet. "Em, I'm sorry." He didn't think his sister could hear him, but he wanted to say it anyway.

Emily came back in, as if she had been standing in the hall waiting for him to say it. "I forgive you, but don't do it again. We have to be able to trust one another, or we can't be a team."

A storm chose that moment to roll through. A clap of thunder startled Emily, and rain began pouring, so the twins spent the rest of the day reading and watching it streak down the windows.

Emily thought about their recent history lesson with their dad. She knew a way to figure out what came next in the story and figure out Fred's question. She took the history book her dad used off the bookshelf and leafed through it. Sure enough, there was the Sugar Act of 1764, the Stamp Act of 1765, and the Townshend Acts of 1767. The next chapter started three years later in 1770.

The colonists wanted to be treated like any other British citizen—with rights and government representation. How could they get the attention of King George III? Would he listen? And if he didn't, then what? She decided to read ahead to figure out the riddle. Tomorrow couldn't come fast enough.

The next morning was still cold and rainy, but the storm passed by the early afternoon. The air felt sharp and cool, as if it had been thoroughly cleaned and hung out to dry in the sunshine. The still-wet grass sparkled. Birds swooped down, wriggled in it for a bath, and flew off in search of worms.

Mr. Tuttle came home from work in time to drive the twins to the lake. "I think I'll do a little fishing on the pier. It's been too long," he said, fetching his tacklebox from the garage.

This made the twins sad; they loved fishing with their dad, but they had a lesson with Fred. Mr. Tuttle smiled at them. "Don't worry. Chances are, I'll end up as part of Fred's plans. His lessons are a lot more interesting than just waiting around for fish to bite."

Lake Ocowoc had four piers, one on each quarter of its oval shape. The north and south docks were extensions of grassy parks with benches and tables for picnicking. The west dock jutted out from a sandy beach where kids swam in the shallows. The east dock, though, wasn't used nearly as much. It stuck out fifty feet into the water, like a wooden thumb from a thick band of trees. The water was deeper and colder there, more dangerous for swimming, but wonderful for fishing. The Tuttles knew it well.

They parked in the gravel patch at the side of the road, exactly at 6pm. Mr. Tuttle grabbed his rod from the truck while the twins ran ahead through the woods, along a thin, dirt path. At the end of the path was the pier. At the end of the pier was Fred... with fishing rods!

"Yay!" Emily shouted, running down the dock. "We get to fish too!"

Ethan was only a couple of steps behind her. Fred smiled as they came running up. "Glad to see you. And you brought your father. He may come in handy."

"Are we going to fish while we learn today?" Ethan asked.

"Well we can try, but the fish in Lake Ocowoc aren't easily hooked." A pile of small crates sat at the end of the dock. Fred chose one and sat down on it, inviting the children to find spots of their own. Ethan didn't remember these ever being there before, but they sure were handy now.

When the twins were seated, Fred asked, "So, what answers did you come up with to my question? How *can* you reason with someone who is being unreasonable?"

Emily went first. "It's frustrating. If you start out talking, but they won't listen to you, then you get louder and louder until you're yelling."

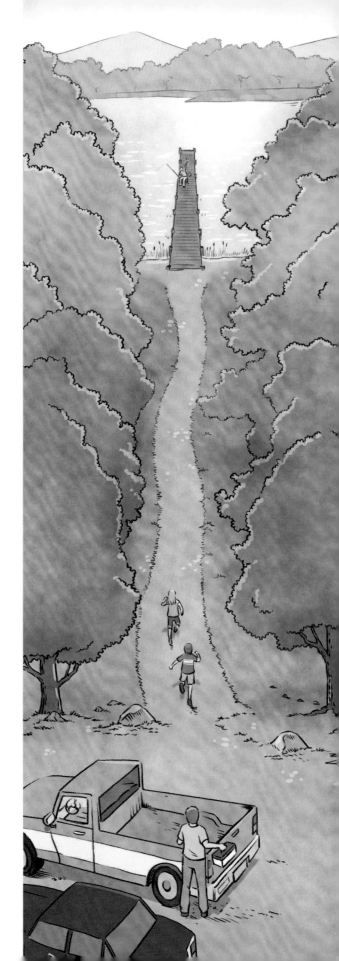

Fred nodded. "And then what?"

"Emily hucks some sour fish at you," Ethan said.

"She does?" Fred said, surprised.

"Only the one time," Emily said, a little embarrassed. "But it's like that, right? I felt like I had to do *something* more than just talk, because he was being stubborn and wouldn't listen..."

"That's very normal. We all want to be understood. And the more important the thing is, the more desperate we can get to have people understand it. Sometimes, people may even resort to physical action, especially when the person not listening is affecting them negatively."

"Sour fish?" Emily asked, sheepishly.

"Or rioting," Fred said.

"The Boston Tea Party!" Ethan said, snapping his fingers. "I knew we were going to talk about that!"

Fred smiled. "It's no good trying to surprise you two. Yes, we're going to talk about the Boston Tea Party. But first we have to talk about another event that had similar consequences. It also happened in Boston."

Emily knew the event Fred was going to talk about because she had just read

about it, but she didn't want to sound like a smarty pants... at least not yet.

"Before I tell that story, though, we should get our lines in the water."

The twins enthusiastically baited their hooks and cast out, their bobbers tossing brightly on the gently rolling water. As usual, on the first cast, it felt like any second a fish would bite, but a few minutes went by with no action. Fred used a lure instead of the bobber method, casting it out and slowly drawing it back in.

"When last we left the Sons of Liberty," Fred said, "they were trying to convince the British government that collecting taxes wasn't going to work—at least, not until they had representation in Parliament. By the way, your father told me about your discussion the other night."

"Yup. We know about 'No taxation without representation,'" Ethan said.

"And we know that the colonists beat the taxes with boycotts and riots," Emily added.

Fred nodded. "The colonial leaders sent many letters to the government in Great Britain—to Parliament, to the King's ministers, and even to the King himself, listing their many grievances and trying to get them to understand."

"Wasn't Benjamin Franklin still in London?" Ethan asked. "If he was there to help, it didn't seem like he was doing a very good job."

"In some cases his recommendations were the reasons people were upset. Still, at this point, most of the anger was directed at Parliament. Even the liberals weren't blaming the King. He was, after all, head of the Church of England, and divinely appointed to be king—or so many people believed."

Emily reeled in and found a fish had taken her bait without getting hooked. "That would have made it hard for people to believe he was also responsible for the bad stuff going on."

"Both of those are correct. It's one reason it was so hard to get some colonists to move from conservative to liberal," Fred said.

"You mean Tory to Whig?" Emily said, before Ethan could.

"Royalist to Parliamentarian," Ethan said, with a smile. He wasn't going to let his sister get all the credit.

A ways back down the dock, they heard Mr. Tuttle laughing. It appeared a big fish had broken his line. Fred glanced that way. "I see you've already had a teacher explain those ideas to you. That makes things simpler. Some people use other names to describe those groups too, and maybe we should talk about that before we get any further. Sometimes, they call them 'good guys' and 'bad guys.'"

Ethan thought for a second. His bobber bounced once, but then was still. "How can we know if one side is really good and the other side bad? The conservatives thought the colonists should have to pay taxes and obey the laws just like everyone else."

"And the liberals evaded taxes and smuggled goods in and out—breaking the law," Emily said. "Wouldn't people call that 'bad' most of the time? But how else were they going to survive so far away from Europe? The British taxes and regulations would have ruined them. Maybe they could have explained that if they had representation in Parliament." She jerked as her bobber bounced, but she had no fish on the line.

"Bummer," she added. "The fish are really winning the battle right now."

"I'm glad you two can see that there are usually at least two sides to every story. And understanding who's right and who's wrong isn't always so easy," Fred said, drawing in his lure. His line came in dripping from the water, with a bare hook. He rummaged in his tackle box. "Think about that as I tell you the next story. It's about an event we call the Boston Massacre."

Ethan cast closer to shore, toward some reeds. That was usually a good spot. "I saw Emily reading about it yesterday. She probably knows all about it."

"Well, not *all* about it," Emily said, glad that Ethan had noticed. "But some, yeah. Because of the Stamp Riots, British soldiers occupied Boston in 1768. There were redcoats everywhere, and colonists were forced to feed and house them too. That's called *quartering*, I think." She looked over at Fred for approval.

"Exactly right," he said, fixing a bright yellow lure to his line. "Keep going. You're doing great."

"The people in Boston hated it," Emily continued, encouraged by the affirmation. "They protested and called for more boycotts of British goods. Mobs roamed the streets looking for tax collectors to rough up. But that made things much worse. And one time, there was a Tory colonist, Ebenezer Richardson, who shot at a mob of children who were throwing rocks at his office. He killed an 11-year-old boy named Christopher Snider."

"That made the people super angry," she added. "Later there was a mob of colonists who surrounded a British redcoat and shouted at him, calling him a child killer. Eventually, they knocked him down with snowballs and sticks. He shouted out for reinforcements,

More About This!

Two Funerals

The procession for Christopher Snider's funeral was two miles long, perhaps the largest gathering in American history to that point! This spectacle was organized by the Sons of Liberty, but it was linked to another funeral in England.

The *Boston Gazette* wrote, "The blood of young William Allen may be covered in Britain. But a thorough inquisition will be made in America for that of young Christopher Snider, which crieth for vengeance."

But who is William Allen of Britain?

Two years earlier, Parliamentarian and celebrity rabble rouser, John Wilkes, insulted the King in his satirical newspaper, *The North Briton*. Because of this, and another highly inappropriate pamphlet, he was sent to prison.

Thousands of Wilkes's fans swarmed the prison. In the chaos, an innocent William Allen was shot and killed by a guard. His death resulted in an explosive riot in the field by the prison, and then spread into other parts of the region, where several more people were killed by British troops. This would be known as the Massacre of St George's Fields.

News reached Boston where Allen's death in Britain soon caused anti-government sentiment to grow. Over the next two years, the Sons of Liberty became pen pals with Wilkes from prison, who encouraged them to keep fighting.

The killing of their own Christopher Snider was the last straw that pushed the Boston Sons of Liberty to a new level of rage.

and then someone began to ring the town bell, like there was an emergency. Everyone poured into the streets and nobody knew what was happening."

Ethan's bobber dunked under the water. "Hey, Ethan," Mr. Tuttle called out. "You've got a fish."

"Forget the fish, Dad," Ethan said. "The liberals are fighting back!"

Emily loved telling stories. Ethan put his chin on his hands and waited for the next part. "The redcoat's call brought a troop of more soldiers to his aid. They lined up to defend their fellow soldier. The crowd waved sticks and threw ice balls, daring the troops to do something about it. All the redcoats were backed up against a wall. They pointed their muskets at the crowd, telling them to keep back!"

"They pointed their guns at the colonists?" Ethan asked in shock and suspense. He forgot all about his fishing for a moment and used his rod like a weapon. "Like this?"

"Like that," Fred said. "Imagine how that would have felt. But surely they wouldn't *fire* at them. Would they really shoot at their *own* people, especially after how the colonists reacted to the shooting of young Christopher?"

"I think they didn't want to," Emily said, "but the people were furious. They used sticks and snowballs as weapons. Finally, someone called out 'Fire!'—and that's what the soldiers did. They shot five of the rioters dead. The crowd exploded, running every which way, crying out that the redcoats were murdering people in Boston."

"Whoa," Ethan said, letting the air out of his lungs. "How horrible. Soldiers shooting their own people? That's only going to make things worse. Did people burn down the redcoats' barracks or something?"

Fred shook his head as Emily tended to her fishing line. "They didn't. But they did arrest the soldiers and put them on trial for murder."

"Good luck to them," Ethan said. "What lawyer would dare try to defend them?"

Fred grinned. "Would you believe... John Adams?"

Ethan's mouth dropped open. "*The* John Adams?! The second President of the United States? *That* John Adams...?"

"That's him," Emily said confidently. "He was also the cousin of Samuel, the founder of the Sons of Liberty. But he still believed everyone was entitled to a fair trial. I think he hoped that by showing the British that the colonists were willing to listen and be reasonable, they would act the same way toward the colonists. He did so well as the lawyer for the redcoats that none of them were convicted of murder."

Fred added, "Oh, and Ebenezer Richardson, the Tory who shot young Christopher? He was pardoned by the King for his loyalty to the crown."

More About Me!

John Adams
Lawyer, Politician

Though a cousin to the rabble rouser, Samuel, John Adams had a significantly more polished reputation. As a distinguished lawyer and legislator, he used his influence to persuade the higher classes of colonists to resist unrepresented taxation, and he eventually pushed for independence from the Crown. Initially, his rhetoric reflected a firm belief in liberalism, but by the time he had become the second president of the United States, his policies were very much conservative, and even authoritarian.

"Well that doesn't sound like a fair trial." Ethan picked up his pole again and reeled in. The fish was gone, along with his bait. "It would have been really hard to get people to calm down after that, and then for the shooters to be let off the hook?"

"Indeed," agreed Fred. "At this point, many people in Boston weren't looking for representation in Parliament anymore. They didn't want to be British citizens—they wanted out. They wanted independence."

Fred's rod bowed. "Fish on!" he said. Then the line sprang back slack. "Fish off. These fish are about as easy to reel in as a Son of Liberty in Boston."

The Last Straw

The sun dipped to the tree line, its rays directly on their faces. "The Sons of Liberty—especially a silversmith named Paul Revere—published reports calling the British murderers and tyrants. The redcoats were so scared they left Boston and moved to Fort William, a little island off the coast. For a while, there wasn't any more fighting. Until the Tea Act."

"I know this story," Ethan said. "A bunch of the Sons of Liberty dressed up as Native Americans and threw three shiploads of tea into the harbor."

"Right," said Fred. "They'd had enough of Parliament making rules without their representation. And this new law gave one British tea company a special tax break that made their tea very cheap."

"Wait, now they're mad because of *lower* taxes?" Ethan said. "Why?"

"If they let that tea be sold in Boston, it would put all the other tea merchants—and even the tea smugglers—out of business," Fred said. "It was another sneaky trick to make the colonists pay them money, but also to interfere with the trading of smuggled products that many colonists actually relied on."

Ethan concentrated on his bobber. He wanted a catch badly. "Parliament is having as much luck getting money from the colonists as we are getting fish!"

"This is just like the unfair law our mayor made to help Bob's Big Barbecue put the food trucks out of business," Emily said. "Sounds like they wanted a monopoly on tea!"

"Exactly," Fred said. "Although the tea belonged to the British East India Company, the ships were actually owned by their fellow colonists."

Emily chimed in. "I read that other than the tea, the protestors didn't do any other damage to the ships. They even swept the deck clear when they left."

"Still, the law-abiding conservatives didn't like the Tea Party one bit. In fact, even George Washington and Benjamin Franklin said they thought it was a bad thing. Franklin went so far as to offer to pay for the ruined tea with his own money."

Ethan stared blankly out over the lake. "Ben, don't you realize it's not about the money? What they want is control."

Emily thought for a moment. "I know you said to be careful about labeling good guys and bad guys, Fred. But the Sons of Liberty had a point. They were only asking to be treated fairly—to have a say in their government. But the British wanted to prove that they were the boss. They wouldn't listen to reason."

Fred nodded. "The Tea Party persuaded Britain that the Americans were uncivilized ruffians and that they needed to be taught a lesson. That lesson was called the Intolerable Acts of 1774, and they were the final straw—the last break between the colonies and their mother country."

"Intolerable... that's a nasty word. Laws the colonists just couldn't put up with," Emily said. "It kind of seems like discussing this reasonably is off the table. And it's going to lead to shooting."

"Yeah, and not with gummy fish, either," Ethan said.

"That is what everyone feared," Fred confirmed. "Just like with the Stamp Act crisis before, delegates from each colony, except Georgia, were elected to meet at The First Continental Congress to prepare a unified response, which became the Articles of Association. This was a significant document, because for the first time colonies officially united as one body to oppose the British Parliament's abusive actions."

The sun was setting as Mr. Tuttle joined them at the end of the dock, and the four of them cast out their lines. Just before true dark, Fred hooked a huge fish, jumping and splashing for five minutes before it reached the pier. Just as he reached the net down to capture it, with a mighty splash, the fish snapped the line and vanished into the deep lake.

They all stood there staring sadly after it. Nobody knew what to say.

Finally Ethan grabbed one of the crates and heaved it into the water. It struck with a splash and floated there on the surface. "Take that, fish! Hope you like tea!"

More About This!

The Boston Port Act

This authorized the Royal Navy to blockade Boston Harbor to any commercial imports or exports. The only imports allowed were provisions for the British army and necessary goods, such as fuel and wheat, until the cost of destroyed tea was repaid. It ensured there would be no illegal trading with foreign competitors and affected everyone, as their economy depended on sending and receiving goods through the port.

The Massachusetts Government Act

This changed the Massachusetts Charter, making local government positions (e.g., council members, judges, sheriffs, jurors) royally appointed, instead of chosen by democratic election. Even public meetings had to be approved by the Royal Governor!

All of this was intentionally focused on disempowering the Sons of Liberty and their subversive tactics.

The Act for Impartial Justice

This act allowed the Governor to relocate the trial of British soldiers, accused of wrongfully killing a colonist, to another colony or to Great Britain for trial!

The act was referred to as the Murder Act because by making it nearly impossible to convict an officer, it enabled redcoats to become more reckless about opening fire on colonists, knowing there would be little to no consequences.

The Quartering Act

The Quartering Act stated that if a colonial town would not provide barracks to British troops, all colonial governors had the power to quarter troops on people's private property!

This was the only act of the four to apply to all of the colonies; it allowed high-ranking military officials to demand better accommodations for troops in uninhabited houses, outhouses, barns, or other buildings at the colonists' expense.

Emily tossed in one of her own. Mr. Tuttle and Fred heaved a couple as well, laughing so hard they could barely fling the crates. The half-dozen boxes now bobbed gently on the swell.

"Nothing like the three hours it took the Tea Partiers to dump all that tea," Mr. Tuttle said, "but strangely satisfying."

"Except I need my crates back," Fred said. "But I wouldn't dare tax you for them."

Emily cranked on her rod. "I bet I can snag them back with my hook."

A mighty splash rocked the surface and then Ethan's head burst upward out of the water. "Never mind that," he said. "I've been dying to cool off!" He seized a crate and dragged it to the dock. "Plus, I need to prove that I can listen when someone says something. It's worth it!"

There was another splash, and Emily swam over to her brother. "I can listen better too. You get those over there, and I'll get these. And you're right—the water is great!"

More About This!

Important Committees and the First Congress
1772–1774

After the Boston Massacre, the Sons of Liberty looked for any opportunity to sabotage or attack abusive British soldiers and officials in the colonies. One such opportunity presented itself in Rhode Island.

Lieutenant William Dudingston was a particularly abusive commander of the *Gaspee* in the Royal Navy. One day, the ship accidentally got stuck in the bay. A band of Sons forcibly removed the crew and set fire to the ship. Some of the band of arsonists were arrested but, similar to the citizens of Boston, the rowdy and rebellious Rhode Islanders had a reputation for producing court jurors who wouldn't prosecute rebellious acts such as this. So, the British government removed that right to be judged by a local jury by sending these political prisoners to London to be tried.

Additionally, in Massachusetts, they changed the way that judges were paid. No longer would their salary be paid by the colonial assembly—they would now be paid directly from the King. This essentially incentivized judges to rule more harshly against rebels and less harshly against abusive British officials.

As soon as this policy was made known, Samuel Adams called for a series of town meetings. He was successful in persuading the assembled council to create, for the first time, a permanent Committee of Correspondence. Usually, such committees were created for specific issues—for example, a committee was called to address the civil unrest around the Stamp Act. But this time, the permanent committee would address the continued usurpations of their rights. He also proposed passing the Boston Resolves, which not only declared their rights as British citizens, but went further by declaring their *natural* rights—ones that are owed to us simply for being human.

The Resolves passed unanimously, which even surprised the liberals. Permanent Committees of Correspondence were set up in dozens of towns, each passing the Boston Resolves. It was clear that the people of Massachusetts were in agreement about this, unwilling to stand for the trampling of their rights any longer. Many more towns also created a Committee of Safety, which would oversee the organization of the militias.

These Committees of Correspondence occasionally sent delegates to a Provincial Congress, which was essentially a replacement government for the old colonial assemblies that had now been taken over by the British government. Under their direction, the many Committees of Safety and the militias might be formed into a larger group in order to defend these newly declared rights from anyone who threatened them… including the British military.

This system was used just a few years later to defend the towns of Lexington and Concord, and also to create the First Continental Congress, in which delegates from all of the colonies were invited to participate. That new Congress unified the colonies under the Articles of Association. The delegates also decided to raise a militia and to not obey the Intolerable Acts. They then decided to meet again in the spring for a Second Continental Congress to take more action!

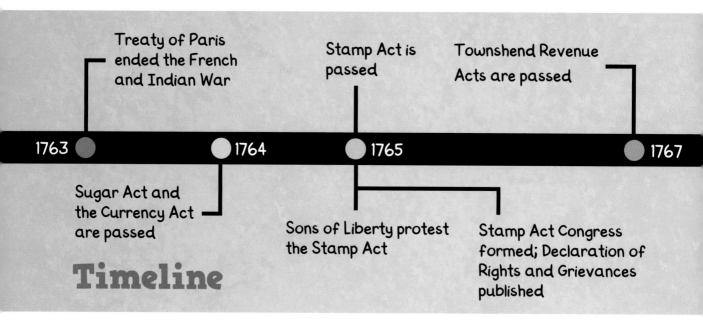

Timeline

1763 — Treaty of Paris ended the French and Indian War

1764

1765 — Stamp Act is passed

1767 — Townshend Revenue Acts are passed

Sugar Act and the Currency Act are passed

Sons of Liberty protest the Stamp Act

Stamp Act Congress formed; Declaration of Rights and Grievances published

A Thought From Connor

People typically don't listen when they fight. In an argument, each side is trying to vocalize its views and assert the correctness of their position. Think of the Boston Massacre... do you think anyone in that environment was sincerely trying to understand what others were thinking or feeling about what had happened?

So much of the conflict in our world comes from poor communication or a misunderstanding about what actually happened. That includes massive wars and family quarrels. It's so important that we try to understand others if we want to persuade them... because after all, it's unlikely that you're going to persuade someone who you're shouting at or attacking.

In battle, this is sometimes referred to as the "fog of war"—a lack of clear information to make good decisions about what is actually happening.

What does that look like in our lives? Well, despite all the information we have access to, we are often bombarded with propaganda and misinformation; some people do this intentionally to try and deceive us. They don't care what we think or feel. As we learn about current events, it's critical that we try to see truth through the fog that surrounds us.

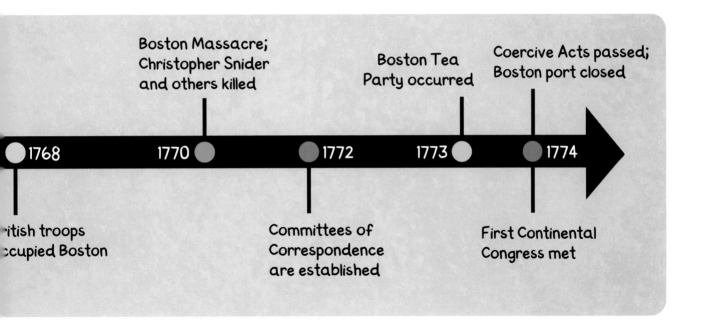

Boston Massacre; Christopher Snider and others killed

Boston Tea Party occurred

Coercive Acts passed; Boston port closed

1768 1770 1772 1773 1774

British troops occupied Boston

Committees of Correspondence are established

First Continental Congress met

Let's Talk About It!

The Sons of Liberty had so much success precisely because so many of the colonists felt that they were being dismissed and disrespected by the British. How would you feel if you felt that your own government was violating your rights and was unwilling to listen to your concerns?

This is why it's important to listen to what others are saying and try to understand how your actions are affecting others. If you ignore criticism and instead push forward to get your way, it may lead to an escalated conflict—and sometimes, to war.

Think of how black people across America felt as they marched for years, petitioning the government (and the public at large) for equal civil rights. Their concerns were often ignored and even ridiculed by those in power. Some black people even joined together to defend themselves from abusive police, leading many white people to consider them radical criminals. (Of course, that's how the British described the minutemen, too...)

How can you do better at listening to people you disagree with?

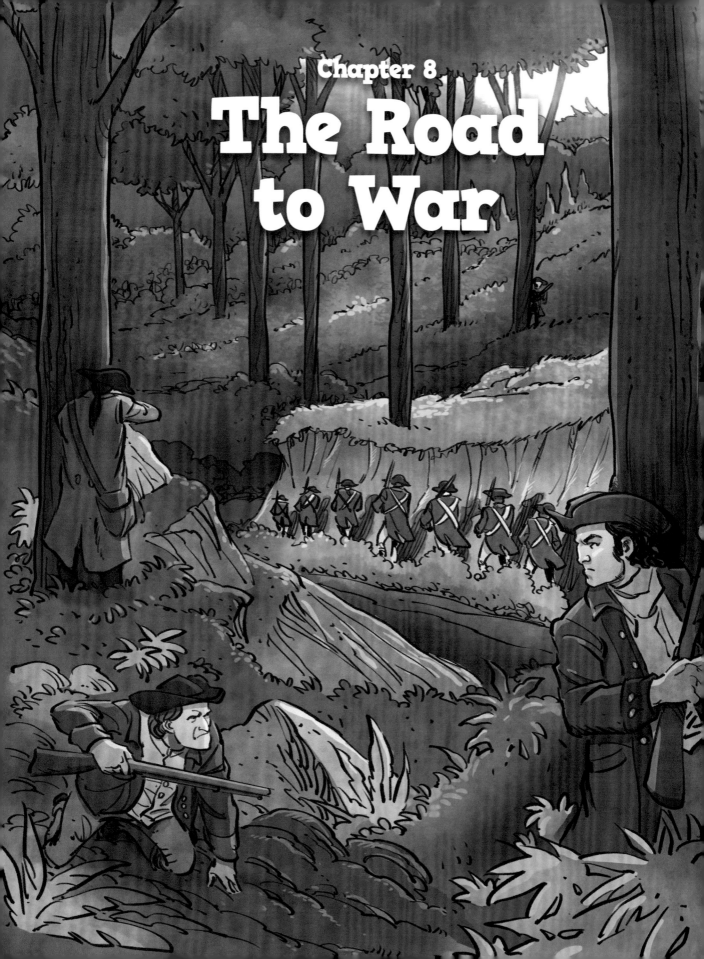

Chapter 8
The Road to War

The Road to Chaos

Fred's backyard never looked like this. Normally it was neatly organized, but now the place had been transformed into a wild obstacle course. Ladders, barrels, poles, ropes, and some old tires lay strewn about the grass as if Jack had planted a tin can instead of magic beans, and instead of a beanstalk, a whole junkyard had grown up overnight.

"Whoa," Emily said. "What happened to Fred's yard? He's taking these lessons to a whole new level."

"There's a note," Ethan said. Large sheets were draped over a clothesline strung between his apple trees making a curtain. A note was pinned on one of them. Ethan read, "Last time, we talked about how when people don't listen, terrible things can happen."

Emily started laughing. "And then we jumped in a lake."

Ethan chuckled as he continued reading, "Today some of those terrible things are going to happen to you." He looked up at Emily with a bewildered face. "What on earth does *that* mean?"

"I'm afraid to find out. But where's Fred?" Emily scanned the yard, but he was nowhere to be seen. The air hung still and quiet, but overhead dark clouds built in the west. "If he doesn't come soon, we might have to go before it rains."

"Wait, there's more," Ethan said. "It says, 'Your obstacle course awaits. Follow the yellow line around the yard, completing each of the obstacles one at a time. Look for the surprise at the end... and the surprises along the way!'" Ethan flipped the paper over and back. "That's all it says."

"It doesn't look too hard," Emily said, craning her neck over the sheet to see more of the apparatus strewn about the yard. Looking closely, she saw yellow paint on the grass, leading in a snaky pattern from one set of obstacles to another.

"Or we could just skip all that and walk straight over there," Ethan said, "to that box on the table, and get the surprise right now. Nobody's watching." At the end of the painted yellow line a large cardboard box, wrapped in Christmas paper, stood on the little table where Fred served them lemonade days before.

"We could," Emily replied, "but if we did, we'd miss the other surprises and lessons along the way. Besides, it will be a lot more fun if we work for it. I bet I can do the obstacle course twice as fast as you can."

"No way!" Ethan said. He charged through the curtain and tripped right into a hidden wading pool filled with water. The splash got almost as much water on his sister as on himself.

"You and water again!" she said, shaking her dripping arms. "Can't you stay dry for even a few minutes?"

Ethan sloshed himself to the side of the pool, water streaming down from his shirt. There in front of them was another note attached to a pole in the ground.

Emily tugged it free and read: "'Congratulations on reaching the first obstacle. Unless I'm very much mistaken, one or both of you will be quite wet now.

That's fitting, because the first part of our story involves the water.'"

"Not this much water, I hope," Ethan said to himself, wringing out his shirt.

"Shhh, there's more," Emily said, continuing to read. "'The British occupiers in Boston realized that if they were going to control the Bostonians they had to control two things: information and ammunition. If the Sons of Liberty could continue to organize and spread radical ideas, they would convince more people to join their rebellion. And if they had the means to shoot back, keeping them in line was going to be impossible for the redcoats.'"

More About Us!

Samuel Adams
1722 – 1803

His Harvard education ended when his father's innovative banking business was outlawed, due to the persuasion of a rival, Thomas Hutchinson. The family fortune was gone and Samuel vowed to get revenge.

From then on, he failed at every business he tried because he was so focused on writing anti-government essays. He rose in political popularity in the early days of the Stamp Act protests—and was no doubt pleased when a mob raided the home of then-Lieutenant Governor Thomas Hutchinson!

His influence really took hold once he met John Hancock, a wealthy businessman who started funding the Sons of Liberty.

John Hancock
1737 – 1793

When his father died, the course of his life changed from future pastor of the church in Lexington to an ultra-successful businessman. His uncle brought him to Boston to learn the family business, where he eventually inherited factories, ships, a mansion, and the most complete general store in Boston.

After the French and Indian War, economic and political turmoil caused tax rioting in Boston. Hancock took a chance on the rebels for two reasons: the taxes were hurting his business, and if the rioters saw him as an ally, it might stop them from burning his businesses and home. After the Stamp Act was repealed, the Sons of Liberty considered Hancock a hero.

"'Therefore,'" the note read on, "'they decided to try to cut the colonists off from both those things at once by raiding a weapons storehouse in Concord and capturing the rebel leaders Sam Adams and John Hancock in Lexington. The rebels couldn't let that happen. See the map on the back.'"

Ethan was already looking at the map while Emily was reading. "Lexington is here, and Concord is here," he pointed out. "Those towns aren't too far from Boston, but it's a long walk. Lexington is ten miles or so, and Concord is another six past that." He peered around the paper at Emily. "They're really going to try to walk that far? 16 miles there and 16 miles back?"

"I guess so. Let's keep reading. "'In the middle of the night of April 18, 1775, redcoats came ashore to march into the countryside and try to capture the two leaders of the Sons of Liberty. They also planned to grab gunpowder and ammunition from a warehouse in Concord. The landing was marshy, and the soldiers had to wade a long distance in the water before they got to solid ground. Wet boots and all, they headed off on the long, dark road to Lexington, unaware that they were being watched—the colonists knew they were coming!'"

The hair on the back of Ethan's neck stood up. All of a sudden, he had that feeling, too—that he was being watched. Even

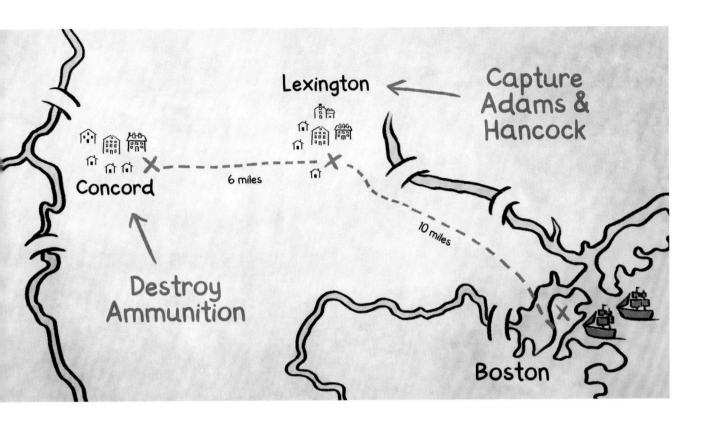

though he was nowhere to be seen, was Fred there watching them? If he were, why was he hiding instead of joining the twins for their lesson?

The Rebels Were Ready

"Let's keep moving," Emily said. The next obstacle looked very simple. There was a short platform, maybe two feet high, and a second platform of slightly greater height only a few feet away.

The yellow line they'd been following showed that they were supposed to jump from one platform to the other. Eyeing it, Emily felt she could almost step between them without having to jump at all. The platform appeared to be solid, and wide enough for both of them to stand on it at the same time, but Emily had already

challenged Ethan to a race. "I'm not waiting for you," she said.

"Wait," he cautioned her, swiveling his head from side to side. "I know we were going to race, but I have a funny feeling about all this. I think we're supposed to stay together."

"What's going to happen? We're in Fred's backyard. We've been here lots of times. There's nothing dangerous about it."

"But where's Fred? Isn't that suspicious to you?" Ethan couldn't shake the feeling of eyes on him.

Emily shrugged. "Grocery shopping? Or maybe we got the wrong time. But I'm going ahead with or without you."

She climbed onto the platform and bent her legs, ready to jump. Without warning, the platform tilted to the left and she almost fell. "What?!" she cried out, arms splayed in the air, trying to keep herself steady.

Ethan grabbed the platform and tried to steady it for her. It wasn't easy. The platform that had looked so solid was now dangerously unstable. "Can you jump to the other platform?"

"I don't know. And what if that one is as shaky as this one? I'll fall for sure." The ground was grassy and soft, but still, she didn't like the idea of crashing onto it.

"Fred's tricky, but he's not going to let us get hurt. I'm sure the other platform is solid," Ethan said, still struggling to keep the platform balanced.

"I'll try standing on the opposite side from you. Then we'll have to jump at the exact same time."

"Got it," Emily said with confidence. She scrunched her face up, concentrating and slid her feet sideways, making sure she didn't move too quickly so that Ethan could climb onto his side while keeping the platform from tipping to one side or another. "We'll jump on three. Ready? One, two, three..."

Together they sprang forward, swinging their feet in front of themselves, trying to land together at the exact same time. They expected some trick, but when they landed, it was like jumping onto the sidewalk. No wobble at all.

More About This!

Colonial Militias

From the earliest days of colonial settlement, a militia would be set up to protect the community from criminals, unfriendly natives, and invaders. This was what police used to look like. Every man over the age of 16 would take a shift on patrol and participate in seasonal training. Unlike the standing army of the British government, the militia was self-governing, organized by the will of its members. Leaders were chosen by vote, and often important decisions were made after group discussion. The members participated not for pay, but as a civic duty, which they took great honor in providing.

In Massachusetts, a select group of skilled militiamen were chosen to receive additional training and were expected to be ready to defend at a minute's notice. These special forces were called the minutemen. For larger conflicts, minutemen from different communities would join together and make a remarkable fighting force in amazing time.

"That's a tricky one," Ethan said. "Still think it doesn't matter if we stay together?"

Emily grinned and nodded her head. "You were right. We definitely need each other for this."

Ethan found another note taped to a pole. "'It was the misfortune of the British that the secret network called the Sons of Liberty was far larger than they had guessed. Riding ahead of the redcoats were men on horseback, spreading the word that *the Regulars were out!* When this alarm was raised, women and men jumped from their beds and quickly took up their weapons.'"

"Ready in a minute," Emily said. "The minutemen."

"'The British, though, had no idea there were militias gathering to fight in the surrounding area. The situation wasn't as stable as they thought, and they were in for a terrible surprise.'"

Ethan lowered the note. "I get it now. This obstacle course is putting us in the shoes of the redcoat army. They thought seizing the ammunition at Concord and arresting John Hancock and Samuel Adams were going to be simple jobs, just like any other day as a redcoat."

More About Us!

Warren's Riders

John Hancock was the leader of the Committee of Safety, which was responsible for organizing the militias in all the towns. When he fled to Lexington to hide, fellow Son of Liberty, Dr. Joseph Warren kept watch. He had two loyal horsemen ready to ride from Boston to Lexington and Concord as soon as the redcoats were sighted, to alert the militias in the surrounding towns

Paul Revere

After his service in the French and Indian War, he returned to silversmithing, a career that introduced him to the prominent families of Boston. When economic troubles and the Stamp Act hurt his silver business, he took up dentistry. It was then he met Dr. Joseph Warren. Soon after, they both became key figures in the Sons of Liberty movement.

William Dawes

A Son of Liberty from the early years, he spent much time recruiting others to the cause. Once, he stole two brass cannons from the redcoats, but in the process he broke his arm. Thankfully, he had Dr. Joseph Warren to help. A year later, Warren called on his friends Dawes and Revere to ride through the country to warn that the redcoats were coming.

Samuel Prescott

This physician from Concord was on his way to Lexington at night and ran into Sons of Liberty Dawes and Revere. He offered to help them on their mission to alert his hometown. On the way, soldiers stopped the three, but only Prescott escaped. Little is recorded about him, though ironically he was the only rider to successfully make it to Concord to alert the militia there.

Solomon Brown

An 18-year-old son of a prominent Lexington farmer, young Solomon noticed redcoats moving into Lexington and helped spread word about their arrival. He was captured, interrogated, and released hours later. According to some reports, he drew fire and may have even been the first to fire his weapon at Lexington, starting the revolution.

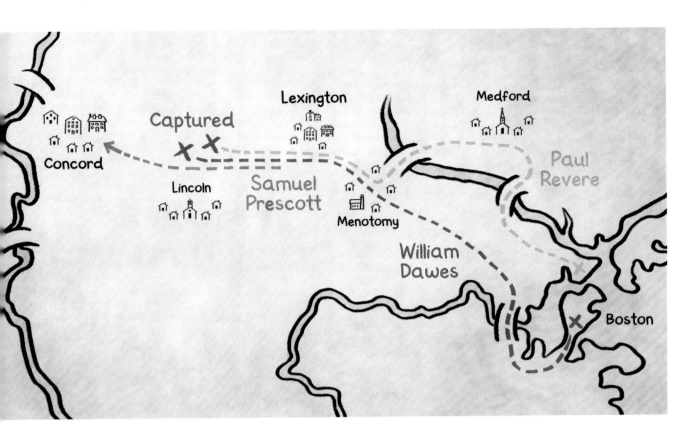

"So, what's the rest of the story?" Emily asked eagerly.

"Oh. Right." Ethan had been looking at yet another drawn map on the other side.

"'Because of the well-organized network of Patriot spies, and horse-riding message carriers, the movement of British troops was communicated to Lexington and Concord very quickly,'" Ethan read. "'This gave the minutemen plenty of time to hide their ammunition and prepare to protect their homes. It also gave John Hancock and Samuel Adams time to get out of Lexington. It's a good thing too, because in their possession was a trunk containing papers with the names of every person involved with the secret Sons of Liberty.'"

"That was close," Ethan added. "Good thing that rider made it when he did."

"Yeah," Emily said. "I guess it's important for everyone to do their job the best they can. You never know when your job will make the biggest impact!"

Emily whipped her head around. "Did you see that?" she asked.

"I was looking at you," Ethan said. "What did you see?"

"I don't know. It was like the trees were moving."

The wind chose that moment to kick up, and the foliage bobbed and swayed around them. "*Everything* is moving," Ethan said.

"No, a tree was moving, like by itself... well, there's nothing there now, at least that I can see. We better go on, and see if we can get it all done before the storm gets here."

The next challenge stood before them. The yellow line led directly to columns of plastic water barrels, stacked two high, taller than the twins. They couldn't see past them, or any way through. "I guess we'll have to climb up," Ethan said. He put his hands on the lip of the top barrel to pull himself up, but the barrels wobbled; they were far too light to hold them up.

Emily watched all this, a curious look on her face. "Wait," she said. "What if..." She stepped forward, put her hands in a gap between one of the columns, and shoved.

The columns of barrels shifted a moment, then toppled over. Emily laughed. "They don't weigh anything at all. We can just push them over."

Ethan backed up a pace and charged the barrels, striking them with his shoulder. The columns burst apart like bowling pins, and in moments the whole barricade lay on the ground in heaps. Ethan wiped his hands together. "That was easy."

"Too easy," Emily said. "Were we even supposed to do that? Maybe the challenge was something else."

"And where's the paper that goes with it?" Ethan asked.

Emily found it taped to one of the barrels, taking a quick look at the new map.

She read, "'At Lexington, the American militia gathered on the wide grassy meadow in the center of town—the Lexington Green. There, the militia and redcoats faced off. *Throw down your arms, ye villains, ye rebels!* the British commander called out. They couldn't believe the colonists would stand with guns against their own government.'"

Ethan snatched the paper from Emily to read the next part, since it was getting good. "'But the minutemen refused to put down their weapons. Infuriated, the soldiers fixed bayonets, and leveled their muskets at the militia, thinking that this show of force would chase off the colonists. A long, tense standoff lasted several minutes. *Don't fire*, the commander ordered his men, but just as he said it, a shot rang out. Both sides fired at one another. The British, though, were better trained, and the American militia scattered, leaving seven dead on the field and nine more wounded.'"

The twins looked around them. On the grass were the barrels they had knocked over, and they lay on the grass like bodies. Ethan gulped. Even though he knew they were just barrels, it still felt... wrong.

Emily took the note back and continued reading. "'The British were shaken to their boots. Had they really just fought a battle with their own people? But there was nothing to do but continue. Hancock and Adams had made their escape, but the gunpowder and ammunition could still be had at Concord, if they hurried. Or so they thought.'"

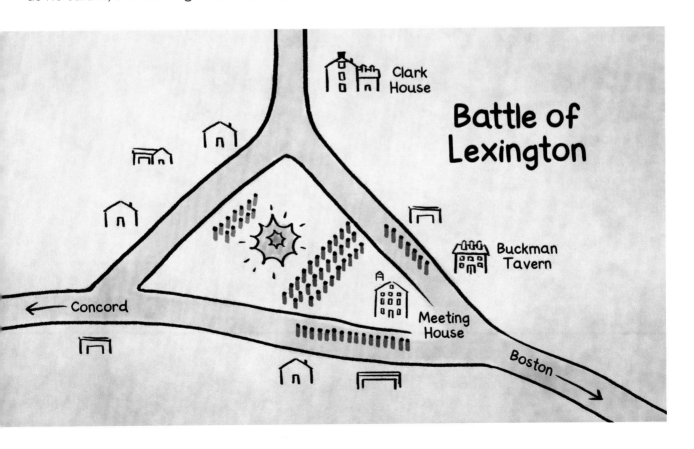

"Next obstacle," Ethan said, but it didn't look like a new one—it looked just like the last one. The same kinds of barrels stood in their way, with the yellow line leading to them just like before.

"At least we know how to take care of this one," Emily said. She marched up to the barrels and slid her hands into the space between the columns to wedge them apart. She pushed. She pushed harder.

Suddenly she heard quick footsteps behind her. "Wait, Ethan—" she began, but she was too late.

He cannoned into the barrels like a football running back, shoulder first.

Their plastic sides bowed in for a split second, then bellied out again, knocking Ethan flat on his back. The barrels hadn't even wobbled. Ethan lay on the grass, stunned. "Ouch."

"They're filled with water," Emily finished. "We can't move them."

"*Now* you tell me!" Ethan said, rubbing his shoulder where he'd crashed into the barrels.

She helped him to his feet. He brushed the grass off while they contemplated the barricade. They could just walk around it, of course, but the yellow line led through, not around. Emily wiped her sweating forehead. The darkening clouds overhead were going to dump rain on them any time now.

"We'll have to climb," Ethan finally said. "At least this time the barrels are heavy enough to hold up."

And they did. Emily clambered up to the top of the barricade and then reached down to help pull Ethan up with her. They clasped hands, and just as they did, something whacked Emily in the side.

"Ow!" she cried out, and let go of Ethan's hand, who fell backward to the grass again.

"Hey! I'm getting pretty tired of having to pick myself up off the grass," he said. "What happened?"

"Something hit me!" Emily said. Another projectile whizzed past her head. She ducked in time, and lay flat on the barrels, hoping that would give her cover. The wind was roaring now, the edge of the storm upon them.

"Who's doing that?" Ethan said, standing up and trying to climb again. A dark sphere whacked into his arm. After already getting bruised twice in under a minute, he barely flinched at the latest injury. "Just keep going," he yelled up to Emily. "They're chestnuts. Someone's pelting us with chestnuts. Can you see who it is?"

"No," Emily said. "But once you get up here, we can get over quickly."

Out of the woods came a steady stream of chestnuts now, thrown or fired with excellent marksmanship. Ethan got to the top of the barrels and rested for a second, arm stinging and shoulder smarting, he looked at Emily. "Whoever that is, they've got one heck of an arm. Almost as good as yours."

"It's Fred," Emily said. "It has to be. But I can't see him, even when I know where to look."

Dust and bits of debris were hitting their faces as the storm intensified. They gritted their teeth and slid along the tops of the barrels, finally dropping to the ground. A paper lay there on a pole. For a moment, the pelting stopped.

"I'm glad he's not going to hit us with missiles while we read his note," Emily said. "We can thank him for that, I suppose."

"Not for much else," Ethan said. "The paper says, 'Samuel Prescott, the only rider who avoided capture, warned the militia at Concord about the approaching army. They immediately got to work, moving their ammunition stockpile from the tavern to a farm across the North Bridge, and up a hill on the outside of town. Other minutemen from around the countryside joined them there after

hearing about what had happened at Lexington.'"

"That was a close one," Emily said. "It seems like one of the lessons here is to have good spies! The colonists know everything the redcoats are going to do."

"Not everything," Ethan said. "Listen to this: 'The British searched the town but found only a few barrels of powder and some old cannons. Frustrated, they threw it all into a fire. The fire blazed up much bigger than they thought it would, threatening the homes. They joined the townspeople carrying water to put out the fire. But from the hillside, the militiamen thought the British were burning the whole town, and they were outraged. They charged toward the North Bridge, where they met a small troop of redcoats who were searching for the hidden ammunition. They faced off against each other, redcoats versus militia, just as they had at Lexington. But this time, the Americans outnumbered the British, and they were in a white-faced rage. When the redcoats fired, the colonists shot back, with deadly effect.'"

"That's the Shot Heard 'Round the World!" Emily cried. "Probably the most famous event of the whole Revolutionary War."

Ethan kept reading. "'They killed several of the redcoats and wounded many more. The British retreated to town to join the rest of the troops. They had thought Concord would be easy, just like Lexington. But it wasn't at all. And now they were wounded, under fire, and sixteen miles from safety.'"

The Redcoats Retreat

Emily stared at Ethan. "Imagine. Surrounded. People shooting at you as you're trying to escape, with 16 miles to march."

Whack! Another chestnut hit Ethan square in the back. "I don't have to imagine it!" he cried, throwing his arms up to protect his head. "Fred's doing it to us right now!"

"Only one more obstacle," Emily said, crouching to present a smaller target. "We can do this."

"Let's do it quickly, then! I'm gonna have bruises all over me!"

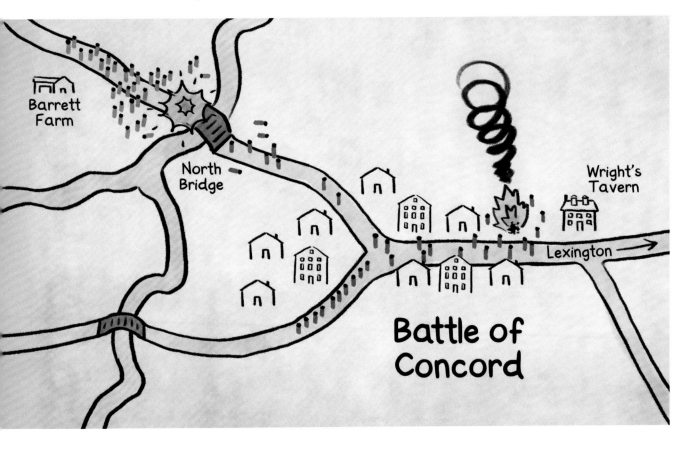

Battle of Concord

The last obstacle wasn't much of an obstacle at all, just an open patch of ground about thirty feet long with ropes stretching over it. The yellow line ran right through it, straight as a jet contrail. But it was bare ground, not grassy, as if it had been plowed, ready for a new garden to be planted. Emily put her foot on it, trying to dodge incoming missiles, but it swallowed her shoe like quicksand.

"Mud!" she said. "And it looks like we're supposed to go under the ropes..."

"Then we crawl," Ethan said, yelling to be heard over the rushing wind. "I'm going to have a chat with Fred when this is over."

They crawled the thirty feet through the mud. It felt like it took years. Chestnuts thumped into them—a bit less often now that they were low to the ground—and slimy mud ran up their arms and legs. Their clothes were coated. At least it didn't smell bad. Ethan was worried that Fred had put manure on his garden. But it was just good clean dirt. Wet dirt. Cold dirt. *So much dirt!*

When they reached the end and could stand up again, the constant fire from the woods ceased like magic. And one last paper was taped to the table where the wrapped box stood.

Ethan plucked the note from the edge, but he plucked too hard, tearing it in half down the middle. "Oh, wonderful," he said.

"It's okay," Emily said, wrapping her muddy arm over his muddy shoulder. "We'll just put the papers together."

She held one side, and he held the other, and together they read:

"'The British retreated that whole day. They were under fire the entire way. Minutemen from every village and farm had been told the British murdered colonists at Lexington and burned the town of Concord. They shot the redcoats down in the road, firing from behind trees, rocks, barns, everywhere. For sixteen miles, the soldiers dragged their dead and wounded down that road, trying to reach Boston. Just before they reached it, a fresh band of militia had gathered from Salem, fresh and full of fight, and they could have cut the troops off from the harbor and destroyed them all. But their commander had compassion on the British soldiers and told his men to let them go.'"

"Kindness," Ethan said. "Just a little kindness."

"It makes a big difference," Emily replied. "I wonder what would have happened if there had been more of that at the beginning. Maybe an awful day could have been avoided."

"If King George III had been kind to the colonists and listened to *them*, none of it would have happened in the first place," Ethan said. "But if I had the chance a minute ago when we were crawling through the mud, I'd have pegged Fred with his own chestnuts. But now... I kind of don't want to."

"Glad to hear that," came a voice from behind them. A walking bush stepped onto the lawn.

It wasn't really a bush, of course. It was Fred, but he'd camouflaged himself so thoroughly he might as well have been a tree strolling onto the grass. He had tied brush to his legs and chest, and his hat was decorated with two branches like antlers.

"I *did* see you!" Emily said.

"Yes. I thought you'd caught me for a second," Fred said, smiling. His white teeth broke out from behind his dark green painted face.

Whack! A chestnut thudded into the center of his chest, and Fred yelped.

Emily tossed a chestnut up in the air and caught it. "Sorry. But you deserved that."

Fred rubbed his chest. "Ethan warned me you had a wicked arm. I see he was right."

Ethan was busy ripping paper off the box that had been waiting for them. "After all that, this better be something great," he said.

But when he opened the box, it was just...

"Groceries?!" Ethan said, mouth gaping. "A sack of flour? A carton of eggs? Two sticks of butter? What kind of terrible joke is this?"

Fred tore his hat off, walking quickly

across the lawn to avoid the drops of rain that began to fall. "I promise when we're done with this, you'll be happy you came and maybe even forgive my obstacle course. But first, let's get inside!"

A flash of lightning suddenly lit the sky, and thunder cracked just a moment behind it.

Ethan grabbed the box, and the twins ran to catch up to Fred.

A Thought From Elijah

I bet before you even read this book, you knew what the colonists' biggest complaint was: no representation! But when they complained and stood up for themselves, the British started taking over their colonial assemblies, too. So now they didn't have a say about *anything*!

Almost no one in Boston was okay with that. Do you know what they did? They started a new government called the Provincial Congress. In many cases, it was just like the assemblies they had before, only... without the British Parliament's permission.

So when those militiamen came running to defend their communities against the invading redcoat army, it wasn't just a handful of gun-toting farmers taking matters into their own hands to overthrow the old government—that's a common misconception that needs to be cleared up. They were acting lawfully (though technically illegally, according to the British) under the direction of an elected government, the Provincial Congress. Now why is that important, and what can we learn from it?

Government is an institution that involves a ton of other people, but in this case, it's not much different than you and a bunch of your friends deciding what to do on the weekend. You can't just make the choice for everyone... Well, you can try, but you won't get a lot of cooperation. Chances are, you'll just end up alone with everyone mad at you. You know that you have to allow everyone to have a say, so you can make a decision that the most people will participate in—that's called creating consensus.

Taking matters into your own hands and forcing your ways of government on a community without their buy-in is just as wrong as when the British did it—even if you know your ideas are the right ones. So what's the solution? You've got to share your ideas and convince others. If they change, then it's voluntary, and you have their consent. But you also have to be okay with them disagreeing—because you can't have *consent* unless people can also *dissent*.

Let's Talk About It!

Authoritarianism is a belief that supposes that leaders or experts have the right to make decisions for everyone else, just like the British soldiers unquestioningly followed the King's orders to attack the colonists.

After World War II, a psychologist named Stanley Milgram wanted to understand how so many German people were capable of committing such horrible acts as part of Hitler's murderous regime. He conducted an experiment to better understand the circumstances in which otherwise good people would do bad things.

Milgram's experiment involved placing the person being studied in front of a machine with a series of switches, each of which would produce an electrical shock that increased in intensity. They were to ask questions of a person on the other side of the wall they could not see. For each wrong answer, the person was told to flip the switch and administer the next biggest shock. As the experiment went on, the person in the other room would scream loudly in pain, demanding the shocks stop. But the authority figure in the room would tell the person they must continue. Shockingly, 65 percent of the participants in the experiment administered the final, massive shock!

Fortunately, the screams were from an actor who wasn't actually getting shocked, but the subjects of the experiment definitely thought it was a real person who they were torturing When asked why they didn't stop even though their conscience told them to, they would often reply that the were just doing what they were told. (This is the same argument Milgram saw Nazis use when trying to justify their war crimes...)

This goes to show the dangers of authoritarianism; many people don't take responsibility for their own actions, instead thinking that the accountability should fall on the authority figure. But when this happens, there may be no end to the horrors they might perform. This is the lesson we learn from Milgram's experiment.

There will likely be a time in your life when you are told to support or do something that you think is wrong. How can you prepare yourself now to avoid falling into the authoritarian mindset and instead take personal responsibility for your own actions?

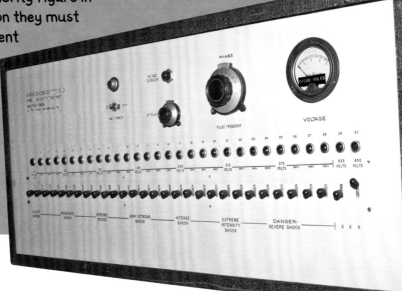

Chapter 9

A Recipe for Cooperation

The Second Continental Congress

"I bet you're wondering what could possibly turn this day into a good one," Fred said.

"I was thinking about that. You always have something interesting," Emily said, rubbing her sore hip, "but your lesson is out of time. We're about to have a storm."

The trees bent under the onslaught of the wind, and even Fred rocked sideways as he walked toward his back door. "You're right about the storm," he said. "Fortunately, part two of this lesson was always going to happen indoors."

A violent crack of thunder split the air. Ethan carried the box of groceries. It was time to get inside, and with not a moment to spare. As soon as they got under the cover of the porch, the rain began sheeting down like a waterfall.

Emily looked sadly over the obstacle course. "All your work," she said, watching the water knock down the papers and soak them. The wet, heavy sheets pulled off the clothesline and fell into the sodden grass. "Your beautiful yard is going to need a lot of cleaning up."

Fred's spirits weren't dampened. He tugged off some of his gear and set it on the porch. He opened his back door and motioned the twins to go on ahead of him.

"But we're covered in mud!" Ethan said. "Do you really want us inside your house like this?"

"You're not much worse than I am," Fred said. "But as it happens, I arranged for a helper to take care of that."

Mrs. Tuttle appeared at the door. She had obviously been watching the entire event from the window. "I brought a change of clothes for you. Did you have fun?" she asked.

The twins spent a minute considering the question as they followed their mother to the bathroom to get cleaned up. "Yes, it was fun," Emily finally said, washing mud off of her arms. "But it wasn't exactly *fun*, the way I usually think of it."

"Parts of it were fun," Ethan clarified, rubbing his sore shoulder and grimacing. "Parts of it were... uh, less fun."

"I promise the next part of Fred's lesson will be the kind of fun you're used to," Mrs. Tuttle smiled.

The twins got themselves out of their wet, muddy clothes and into dry ones. They came back into the kitchen, where

Mrs. Tuttle had taken all the groceries and spread them out on the counter.

"What's this all about, Mom?" Ethan asked.

"You'll see. I don't want to ruin Fred's surprises. Why don't you tell me about what you learned from the obstacle course."

Both twins explained their adventure with the platforms and the barrels and the mud. "And the chestnut bullets," Emily said. "Fred can really chuck them. But it helped us feel a little bit of what it might have been like for the redcoats on that terrible day."

"Fred really can tell a story, though," Ethan said. "I'm learning so much! He doesn't just teach facts—anyone can teach those—but also *why* things happened and how it might have felt to be there, struggling with what's right and wrong in a world of new ideas."

"And what it means for us all these years later," Emily said. "I had no idea the same struggles from history are still playing out today... like this story hasn't ended yet."

A few minutes later Fred reappeared, toweling off his ears. "Camouflage face paint is the worst. I can never get it out of my ears! So, do we have all our ingredients ready to go?"

"I think so," Ethan said. "But this is a lot of stuff. I'm not sure what it will make."

"I know what we're making," Mom said. "And I think you'll like it, but I will confess; it has a lot more ingredients than *my* recipe."

"That's because it's a special recipe," Fred said, hanging up his towel on a peg on the wall. "Let's start with the dry ingredients. Emily, you'll find measuring cups and spoons in the bottom drawer in front of you. Start with three cups of flour. Ethan, you bring a big bowl and the mixer over."

Everyone got busy and in a few seconds Ethan had a big bowl placed in front of Emily who was measuring flour, being careful to make sure she got exactly the right amount. Fred took out a big three-ring binder filled with recipes, opened to

a page, and displayed it on the counter.

"Ohhh," Ethan said, cocking his head so he could read. "Continental cookies? Mom was right—I *am* going to like this."

"Almost makes up for the chestnut missiles," Emily said, laughing.

Ethan picked up a bag of brown sugar with a name taped to it. "Look, South Carolina."

Emily held up the bottle of vanilla in one hand and a bag of coconut in the other. They also had names: "New York" and "Connecticut."

"Tell me how many ingredients are there on the page?" Fred asked. Emily counted.

"Thirteen," she said. "Hey, like the thirteen colonies and the Continental Congress!"

"Get it now? Continental cookies," Fred said. "You can imagine what was in store for the thirteen colonies once word of the British defeat at Concord reached London. Ships of redcoats and German mercenaries, called Hessians, were already on their way."

"Delegates were again summoned from each of the thirteen colonies for a Second Continental Congress that convened on May 10, 1775. They were faced with several problems, but they couldn't agree on how to solve them. Should they fight their own government or should they try to make peace? If they did fight, should they do it as thirteen small militias or one unified continental army? Who would lead the army and how would the fighting be paid for?"

"Well, they'd better hurry up," Ethan said impatiently. "Patriot militias have already started fighting, and the British army and navy are coming their way! There's not a lot of time to be sitting around talking."

"You're absolutely right," Fred agreed. "But even after what happened at Lexington and Concord, the colonial leaders were still far from being united. Most still believed King George III would relent and listen to their concerns."

"How are all these different ingredients going to come together to make something delicious in time?" Mrs. Tuttle asked. "It seems impossible."

"The flour is Massachusetts—the center of the conflict, which was in Boston. They're already at war and desperately want help from the other colonies," Fred explained. "What comes next?"

"Baking soda and baking powder, one tablespoon of each," Mrs. Tuttle said.

Fred stood back from the counter and let the Tuttles go to work. "I'll let your mom oversee the mixing," he said, "so I can tell you about the history lesson that goes along with these cookies. The baking soda and the baking powder are two very important ingredients that represent voices from two very important colonies, Pennsylvania and Virginia."

Ethan scraped the tablespoon of baking soda level, and dumped it in the bowl. Emily repeated the process for the baking powder, fixated on Fred's explanation.

"One very important thing we have to do is make the ingredients rise together, the same way the Patriots need to get the colonies to rise up together against the British. But not everyone responds the same way—kind of like the baking powder and baking soda there in the bowl. Take a look."

Ethan thought that if he looked carefully, he could just barely tell the difference between the white of the flour and the white of the baking soda and powder. "What exactly are we looking for?" he inquired.

"Baking soda is activated by liquid," Fred said pointing in the bowl. "When it gets wet, it reacts. Baking powder, though, is activated by heat. When it gets hot, it goes to work. The two look the same, but they aren't, even though in the end they both make the cookies rise so they're not undesirable lumps of flour and sugar."

Pennsylvania

"So what did the delegates from Pennsylvania do that helped the colonies rise up?" Emily asked.

"I bet you can guess who one of the delegates was," Fred said. "Of all the colonies, Pennsylvania was still very loyal to the King—lots of Tories. At this time, the majority of the colonists were also loyal to the royal. But imagine if a famous Tory joined the Patriots—it might convince others to follow."

"Hmm. A Tory from Pennsylvania..." Emily thought out loud. "Is it... Benjamin Franklin?"

"You got it!" Fred said, extending a high five to Emily. "Benjamin finally came home from London and arrived just a few days before Congress convened. It seemed he had given up on trying to be friends with Parliament after they voted for the Intolerable Acts against his people in America."

"Yes! Finally Ben Franklin is joining forces with the liberals—the Patriots!" Ethan said.

"At least for the cause of fighting the British, yes. He's going to join their side," Fred said. Mrs. Tuttle added the other dry ingredients to the bowl—cinnamon for Georgia and salt for Rhode Island.

"Pennsylvania also had a large population of Quakers. They were religious people who believed in being loyal to their governments. They were also Tories and pacifists, which means they did not support fighting. John Dickinson, one of the delegates, was raised a Quaker, and still shared many of those beliefs. He wouldn't agree to form a continental army unless Congress made one more attempt to petition the King to stop the fighting. This letter was called the Olive Branch Petition. If the King still refused peace after that, then he and many other people would add their support to the Patriot cause."

"I guess that sounds like a reasonable compromise, especially if it brings more Tories to join, but..." Ethan put his elbows on the counter in frustration. "There's no time. Sending a letter by ship takes... "

"More than a month," Fred said. "The British military will be here before the letter even gets to London."

"They can't wait that long!" Emily said. "They have to do something now."

"I agree, and so did the Congress. They had to choose a commander to organize the militias in the meantime," Fred said. "Like gunpowder, baking powder activates in the heat of battle."

"Virginia," Mrs. Tuttle interjected as she walked over to preheat the oven.

Choosing a Commander

"Until this time," Fred continued, "the Continental Congress organized boycotts and sent letters. Now they were about to do something very big—choose a leader to fight against their own government.

More About Us!
The Quakers of Pennsylvania

The Society of Friends was founded in 1652 by George Fox of England. They were often observed "quaking" (or shaking) when they worshiped, earning them the nickname, The Quakers. They were focused on their personal relationship with God, rather than on ceremonies and religious hierarchy. This put them at odds with others who, at the time, were hyper-focused on religious conformity. Their beliefs lead to their brutal persecution.

A Quaker friend of Charles II, William Penn, asked a special favor of the King—to establish an experimental colony in America in which all people could practice their faith under a government of Quaker leadership and by the principles of tolerance, respect, and friendship. The request was granted. The colony was named Pennsylvania after Sir Penn. It was one of the first major groups to advocate for the abolition of slavery and the rights of natives.

Virginia

Who should it be? There were lots of candidates, most of whom were experienced, able leaders with long track records of success in battle. However, two very good—but very different—candidates came out of Virginia."

"Obviously George Washington," Ethan said, "the hero from the French and Indian War." He thought for a moment. "Actually this whole argument about taxes, representation, and rights really started way back then—that first battle when George was only 22 years old."

"I wish that battle never happened," Emily sighed. "None of this fighting would have started: the world war, the taxes, the Boston Massacre, the Tea Party..."

"Fascinating to think about!" Mrs. Tuttle said. "But then we might not have this country, the first one of its kind that put individual liberty and personal rights as a priority." She had finished combining the butter, eggs, sugar, and vanilla in the bowl and turned the mixer on.

"You're right, Mom," Ethan said. "It didn't start with George Washington. It started because of all those dumb empires going to war all the time, when they could have cooperated in peace and trade."

"Who was the other candidate to be the commanding officer?" Emily asked, getting back on topic.

"His name was Charles Lee," Fred replied. "He was from England and fought many battles for the King—very experienced. He was also a Whig, a radical liberal, a true believer in human rights and freedom. He moved to Virginia years earlier to support the colonies in their protests against British abuse. His strategy was to continue fighting in the guerrilla style, avoiding big battles and hitting the British where they least expected it."

"Gorilla style?" Emily said, lumbering about the kitchen and making "ooo aaa" noises like an ape.

Everyone laughed. "No, not gorilla.

Guerrilla. It's a Spanish word meaning to fight in a non-traditional way, quickly and quietly, in small groups, with no big battles," Mrs. Tuttle said.

"Just like the minutemen at Concord," Fred said, ducking down behind the bar and pointing his finger like a gun. "My guerrilla tactics sure worked well on the obstacle course against you two. Many of the delegates at the Continental Congress thought Charles Lee was the perfect choice."

"I'd also choose him," Ethan said. "He sounds perfect!"

"I've never heard of him, though, so I guess he didn't get the job," Emily said. "What happened?"

Charlie, your guerrilla strategy is certainly *ape*-pealing.

Thank you, but the Congress seems a bit *split* about that.

More About This!

Charles Lee & Guerrilla Warfare

In traditional warfare, wars were fought primarily through pitched battles, where each side anticipated the other, agreed on a location, and openly fought against one another. This is how British soldiers fought. But many colonists used guerrilla warfare tactics, a less formal approach that involved attacking the enemy when they least suspected it.

This approach was favored by Charles Lee, an experienced British soldier who became inspired by the liberal philosophy of John Locke and the Whigs. He moved to America and became friends with Thomas Jefferson, Samuel Adams, and other Patriots. Lee was ready and willing to take up arms to defend against the British, but many of the colonists did not believe that they could stand up to the biggest military force in the world.

Lee published a short book in which he described his experience with the British military and included his observations of their weaknesses. He didn't believe they were that great, and he was confident that the locals could win because the Americans outnumbered the redcoats, and they were far more familiar with the countryside. He believed that by using guerrilla warfare, they could beat the British. The booklet sold out five times and gave the Patriots courage.

When he was presented at the Second Continental Congress as a candidate to lead the Colonial Army, Lee's resume was very impressive. He planned to train the men in the guerrilla tactics they were already familiar with, but after some debate, George Washington was instead chosen.

Fred nodded. "Being the Colonial commander had to be more than just the person with the most experience and best strategies. Remember, the colonies were divided—Tories and Whigs, conservatives and liberals, loyalists and patriots, and many more who didn't care about who was in charge of the government at all. A radical liberal and a guerrilla fighter like Lee would have encouraged the other liberal guerrilla fighters, but what about the others who disagreed?"

"The more that people could be united, the better chance they had at victory," Mrs. Tuttle said. The dry ingredients were now in the mixing bowl with the others. Emily turned the mixer on and the powerful motor pushed the blade around. The ingredients turned to sweet-smelling dough as they mixed together.

"Washington wanted England and other countries to see them as a real army and not just snipers behind trees and arsonists in the night. He envisioned something to inspire the colonists too. Whoever took command would have to be someone *all* the people could look up to and support." Fred scooped balls of dough from the mixing bowl and then squished them into flat circles on the cookie sheet. "Smells delicious…"

"George Washington was the ingredient that made the others rise together to battle," Emily said. "Some might not have joined if he hadn't been chosen."

"The Continental Congress decided that Washington was the man they needed to lead them against the redcoats," Fred said. "He was brave and popular. He was tall and strong. And, maybe more than anything else, he was neither a liberal Whig nor a conservative Tory—just a good man whom most people liked and respected. He was also well known in England, remember? Putting him as head of the continental army would be quite a statement."

"It took the Congress a month to make their decision," Mrs. Tuttle said, putting the cookie sheet in the oven, and setting the timer for 12 minutes.

"But a month is how long it takes to sail from London to Boston," Ethan said. "That means the troops would have already arrived!"

"Correct," Fred said, giving him a thumbs up. "Washington was appointed as Commander-in-Chief of the Continental Army on June 19, 1775—two days *after* a Patriot militia suffered a terrible defeat at Bunker Hill in Boston."

"I've heard about the Battle of Bunker Hill, but I don't know what happened," Ethan said. "Can you tell us about it while we wait for the cookies?"

Bunker Hill

Fred smiled and was all too willing to keep the story going. "The first few battles of the Revolutionary War involved the Patriot militias securing guns, ammunition, and cannons that the redcoats were trying desperately to seize," he said. "All of these were important victories for the Patriots, because without weapons they'd have no way to defend themselves."

"But the Battle of Bunker Hill was very different, and it left so many dead on both sides that it permanently ended any chance that either side would forgive and forget. I asked your mother to come— partly to bake cookies, of course—but also to tell the story of that battle."

Mrs. Tuttle settled against the counter and began. "Bunker Hill is famous, but oddly, the battle was mostly on nearby Breed's Hill. Both of those hills overlook Boston Harbor, and if the Patriots were able to put cannons there, they could sink every British ship that tried to come to shore. So the Commander-in-Chief of the British army, William Howe, ordered the redcoats to drive the Patriots off those hills."

"They should know by now that Boston's Patriots aren't going to back down," Ethan said, rubbing his hands together. "Especially after all of the victories so far."

More About This!

Virginia's Gunpowder
Patrick Henry

When it became clear that a fight was coming, Royal governments began to quickly seize the gunpowder and ammunition in the colonies. In Virginia, Governor Dunmore's men took the gunpowder from all the stores. Henry knew they'd have no chance of fighting back if they didn't retake the confiscated ammunition. George Washington and Robert Henry Lee said the plan was too risky, so Henry led his militia himself. They were successful in returning the ammunition that would soon be needed for the war ahead. To other Patriots, Henry was a hero. But Governor Dunmore declared him an outlaw.

Ft. Ticonderoga
Benedict Arnold & Ethan Allen

As soon as news of Lexington and Concord reached Connecticut, a brave Patriot merchant named Benedict Arnold started marching his militia toward Fort Ticonderoga in northern New York, close to the border of Canada. He knew that many cannons were stored there. Without them, the future Colonial army wouldn't stand a chance against the British army and navy. Along the way, he met another militia called The Green Mountain Boys, led by Ethan Allen. They had the exact same idea. They joined forces and caught the British off guard. Their troops took control of the fort and secured valuable cannons and ammunition that General Washington would eventually need to win back Boston!

"Bunker Hill wasn't going to be like that," Mrs. Tuttle said. "This wasn't a stretch of road with forest on either side. The British knew right where the Patriots were. They were dug in, right at the top of the hill. This time, they could attack without being afraid of guerrilla tactics. Their mission was simple: climb a hill and take it over. The British thought that this time the Patriots would run. They didn't."

The smell of warm cookies started to permeate the air. Ethan's tummy growled. "Just a few more minutes," he said, checking the timer.

Mrs. Tuttle continued, "The Patriot militias from the surrounding villages and towns were determined to hold their position. They waited until the British were almost right next to them. One of the officers, William Prescott, told his fellow militiamen, 'Don't fire until you see the whites of their eyes.' And when the time was right, they fired. It was devastating. It broke the British charge and sent them running back down the hill. But Howe, the Commander-in-Chief, sent them right back up. Once again, the Patriots fired at point-blank range and shattered their ranks. By now, the hill was littered with bodies and equipment. The Patriots wondered if there would be enough soldiers to come at them again. The British couldn't believe the militiamen were able to stand up to their firepower."

"The Patriots are winning!" Emily said, clasping her hands.

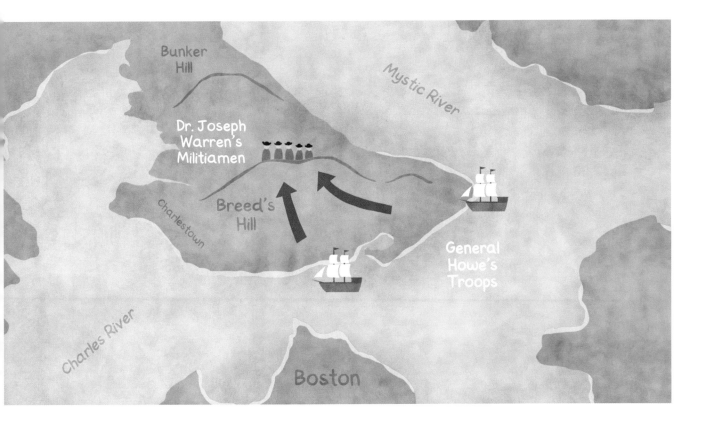

The timer for the cookies dinged, but the twins didn't want to miss a word of this story. Fred put on his oven mitts, removed the hot cookies from the oven, and started placing them carefully on a cooling rack, while Mrs. Tuttle continued.

"The British made one final charge, but this time the Patriots ran out of gunpowder. The final minutes of the Patriots' stand were fought with bayonets."

"Ooh!" Ethan squirmed, thinking of being run through by the little swords at the end of a musket. He subconsciously patted his abdomen with his hand. "Awful."

More About Me!

Joseph Warren
Physician, Politician

- Leader of Boston's Committee of Correspondence
- Enlisted the midnight riders, Paul Revere and William Dawes, to spread the alarm that British soldiers were coming to Concord
- Participated in the battles at Lexington and Concord the following day
- Commissioned as a major general in the militia shortly before Battle of Bunker Hill
- Fought alongside his militiamen and was killed atop Breed's Hill

"Not much worse than having a lead ball the size of a grape ripping through you at 1,200 miles per hour," Fred interjected.

"Good point."

"The British overcame them, took the high ground, and slaughtered almost everyone they captured, including Dr. Joseph Warren, who was the Patriots' commander," Mrs. Tuttle said. "The Patriots had lost that important battle, the hill, and Boston—but they had proven to the British that defeating the Patriots wasn't going to be easy."

A few minutes later, a plate of big, beautiful cookies and four tall glasses of milk stood on the table. Ethan started handing out the cookies. "No doubt, Mom. These continental cookies came together after all, just like the Continental Congress. Good thing there were some Tories in Pennsylvania willing to compromise with the radical liberals. Now Congress is unified in their treason against the King."

"And I guess that means Washington was the right choice," Emily added. "Maybe if he had been leading the soldiers at Bunker Hill, his traditional method of fighting would have helped there."

"Well," Fred said, "Washington *was* the man they chose, and the colonies *did* win the war and become a new nation—so it's easy to say now that he was the right choice. But I sometimes wonder if the war might not have been over sooner if we'd chosen Charles Lee instead. I guess we'll never know for sure."

"I know *this* for sure," Emily said, her mouth half full of cookie. "This lesson is way less painful than the last one!"

Everyone raised their glass and cheered in agreement!

A Thought From Connor

Imagine for a moment that you're George Washington. You've just been given control of the Continental Army and you're tasked with taking on the strongest military superpower in the world.

And you have to do it with a bunch of untrained and untested farmers with rifles.

How would you feel? Would you be confident about your ability to succeed? Chances are, you'd wish for better circumstances to increase your odds of beating the British.

You'd probably wish for more funding, more ammunition, more troops, more favorable battlefields, and much more to improve the poor condition of the army you now oversee. But what does wishing get you?

Here's the lesson: we have to work with what we have. Washington knew this and set out to do the best he could. Even if we want to make bold steps forward for freedom, we have to start somewhere. And sometimes we have to start in circumstances that are less than ideal—such as in a state that has high taxes and regulations, in a community full of socialists, in a school with authoritarian teachers, or in a family that doesn't believe in freedom.

Whatever our circumstances, we can focus on taking incremental steps in the right direction. Some of Washington's problems didn't go away for a very long time; his soldiers had long suffered with poor nutrition, inadequate medical care, and tattered clothing. They struggled for months, waiting for relief.

And sometimes, those sacrifices are worth it— because what we're fighting for doesn't require us to have the best circumstances. It just means we have to be willing to put in the work and move forward, one step at a time.

Let's Talk About It!

Would you eat a cookie that was made without sugar? What about if the flour and baking soda were missing? Which ingredients could you remove and still consider eating it?

Each of the colonies had their own interests; they were unique and contributed different things. The Continental Congress had to figure out the right balance between these "ingredients" as they debated what to do about their common interests and objectives.

This same idea can apply to our communities, where things improve because of the contributions of different groups, churches, and families. And your own family is like this, too—each person is different and makes the overall family better. Your family wouldn't be the same without each of its "ingredients," including you!

As a family, use the following recipe to make your own continental cookies. While you're waiting for them to bake in the oven, take turns pointing out another family member's "ingredient" and how it contributes to your family being as great as it is.

Continental Cookies

INGREDIENTS

3 cups all-purpose flour
1 tablespoon baking powder
1 tablespoon baking soda
1.5 tsp ground cinnamon
1 teaspoon salt
1.5 cups butter (room temp)

1.5 cups granulated sugar
1.5 cups light brown sugar
3 large eggs
1 tablespoon real vanilla
3 cups rolled oats
2 cups flaked coconut sweet

1.5 cups butterscotch chips

Recommended extras:
2 cups chopped pecans
1.5 cups mini semisweet chocolate chips

1. Preheat the oven to 350°. Line baking sheets with parchment paper or silicone baking mat.

2. In a medium bowl, mix the flour, baking powder, baking soda, cinnamon, and salt; set aside.

3. In a large mixing bowl, beat the butter on medium speed until smooth and creamy, about 2 minutes. Gradually beat in the sugars and continue to beat until light and fluffy, scraping the bowl as necessary, about 3 minutes. Add the eggs one at a time, beating well after each addition. Beat in the vanilla extract. Reduce the mixer speed to low and gradually add the flour mixture, mixing until combined. With a wooden spoon or large rubber spatula stir in the chocolate chips, oats, coconut, and pecans.

4. For each cookie, using a 1/3 measuring cup to scoop out dough, drop dough onto the baking sheets. You can fit 6 on a half sheet sized pan. Gently press cookies a few times to flatten them down a bit so they will bake evenly. Bake until the edges are set and slightly golden, but the middles still look light and puffy, about 12 minutes, rotating the sheets halfway through. Cool cookies for 2-3 minutes on trays, remove and cool completely on wire racks. The later batches may bake in less time—watch them carefully! Yields about 3 dozen.

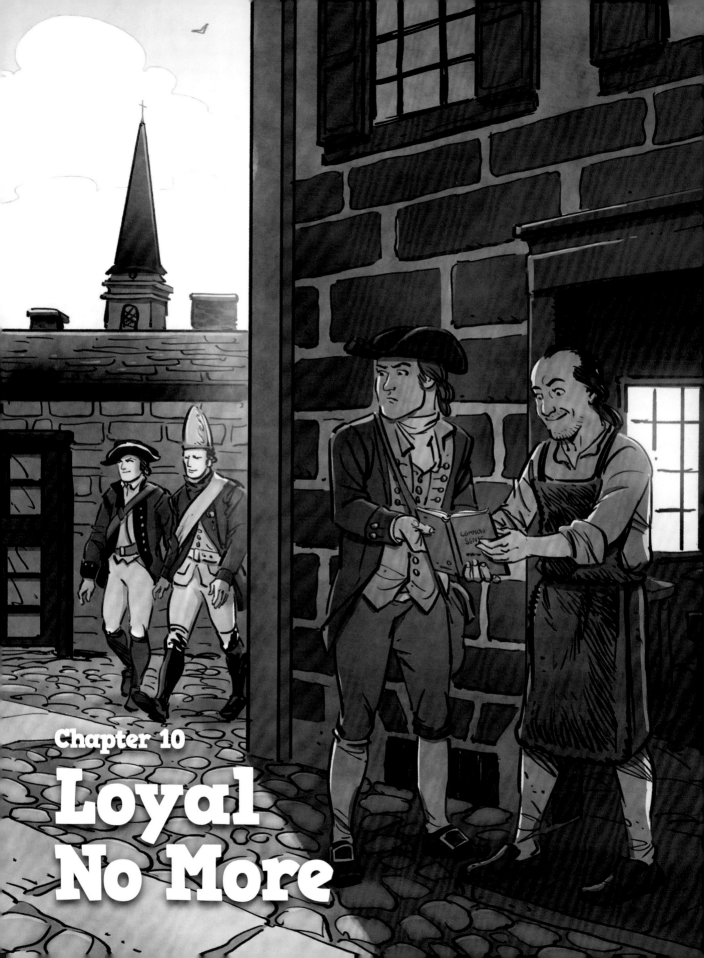

Chapter 10
Loyal No More

Men of the Continental Congress

Fred was rolling the last of the water barrels across his yard, whistling a tune. He stacked it with the rest next to his shed, just as the twins finished collecting the chestnuts from the lawn.

"Anything else we can do to help?" Ethan asked. "There are still some tires left from the obstacle course to clean up."

"No, no, but thank you," Fred said. "That's good enough for now. But there are surprises waiting for you on the desk in my office. You look them over, and I'll be there in a moment."

Emily led as they went inside and up the stairs to the office with its tall bookshelves lined with nearly every kind of book. She loved to stand close to them with her nose close to their spines and take a deep breath. They smelled so good! The older they were, the better they smelled. Fred had some very old books in a special corner. For Emily, standing there felt like she was standing next to the past.

Ethan, however, went straight for Fred's desk. There, he found a plate of continental cookies, and two stacks of cards. "Cool!" he said. "Baseball cards! I love these."

But when he looked closely at them, they weren't what he had thought. The pictures did not have smiling, bat-waving men on them. Instead, the people were in formal clothes—coats, fancy colonial ties, some of them even in powdered wigs. "What's this?" he said. "These aren't like any trading cards I've ever seen before."

Emily took a break from loving the books to join Ethan sitting by the desk. She picked up one of the stacks and thumbed through it. "Caesar Rodney. Robert Morris."

Ethan read a couple of his. "Lyman Hall. William Whipple."

Emily frowned, concentrating. "I feel like I know these names from somewhere. They're familiar."

"This one will be," Ethan said, holding up a card. "John Adams. No prizes for guessing who that is."

"Look at the backs," Emily said, flipping her card over. "There's all kinds of info about who they are and what they did."

"Like this one—this is Samuel Chase," Ethan said. He read, "'Chase was a delegate from Maryland to the Second Continental Congress. He signed the Declaration of Independence. After the war he was made a Supreme Court justice. He was the first member of the Supreme Court to be impeached, though he was not convicted. Chase was a mercantilist and a conservative in the Congress, but voted in favor of independence.'"

The twins looked at each other. Ethan said, "Mercantilist. Conservative. It's nice to know what those words mean."

"Listen to this one," Emily said. "It's about George Clinton. 'Though he served with the British in the French and Indian War, Clinton was loud in support of independence. He was a delegate to the Second Continental Congress but he did *not* sign the Declaration of Independence, because New York's delegation did not get permission to sign it until after he had resigned. He served as a militia commander in the Revolutionary War and eventually was elected Vice President under Jefferson *and* Madison. He was a Whig, and a radical liberal.'"

"There's 'Whig.' That's another one we know," Ethan said.

"And 'radical liberal,' a freedom fighter."

"Indeed—and we have a lot to discuss today about those things and others," Fred said, coming up the stairs and peeling off his gloves.

"Did you make these cards?" Ethan asked. "They're wizard!"

Fred scratched his head, puzzled. "Wizard? Is that good?"

The twins laughed. "It's *very* good," Emily said. "He likes using that word."

"I will never be able to keep up with how your slang changes," Fred said. He thumped down in his desk chair. "Take another few minutes and look through those cards. What's something all those people have in common?"

The twins sorted through the cards and tried out ideas. Some were conservatives, some liberals, some somewhere in the middle. They were from all the different colonies. Many were quite young in their pictures, but some were older. Most had signed the Declaration of Independence, but there were those like George Clinton who had not. Then Emily got it.

"The Second Continental Congress!" she cried out. "Every one of these people was at the Second Continental Congress."

JOHN HANCOCK

"That's right," Fred said. "Can you tell me about that?"

"They made George Washington the Commander of the Colonial Army," Emily said. She opened her mouth to say more but realized she didn't have much to fill it with.

Ethan said, "And they issued the Declaration of Independence. But... I don't know much else."

"Perfect. We'll have lots to talk about." Fred settled himself a bit deeper into his chair and motioned for the twins to pull up chairs of their own.

"Last time we chatted, the Congress appointed George Washington to organize all the colonial militias and they also sent the Olive Branch Petition. The conservative Tories believed that if the King would only read it, that surely he would help his own subjects. Any day now, they hoped, things would settle back down. So they waited for the reply."

Ethan shook his head. "That's not going to happen, especially not after all the dead at Bunker Hill. And Washington is already fighting some new battles, right?"

JOHN DICKINSON

Uniting for Independence

"But what other options did they have?" Fred inquired. "If they weren't British, or Dutch, or Spanish... what *were* they?"

"Themselves," Emily said. "They were Americans."

"But many weren't ready to start thinking like that," Fred said, leaning forward. "In fact, even at the beginning of 1776, most people just wanted to end the Coercive Acts, and they wanted some kind of representation in Parliament. Remember, it took a lot of convincing and compromise to get the Congress to even agree to defend themselves against the redcoats at all. The idea of starting their own governments wasn't even a serious consideration. There were so few people really thinking about being *independent* that John Adams wrote to Thomas Jefferson and told him not to bring it up yet, because that was considered treason by most people."

"Are the continental cookies part of this lesson about the Continental Congress?" Ethan asked while licking his lips. "I'm getting hungry."

"That's exactly what they're for. I have milk too." Fred fetched a carton from the mini-fridge next to his desk.

"Or perhaps tea and English biscuits, instead? In case you're not quite ready to be independent yet..."

The twins laughed, then began eating.

Back around the desk, Fred shuffled through cards. "Here's the big question, and the subject of our lesson today," he said, dealing out the cards. "How is it that in January of 1776 almost no one was even talking about independence, but by July of the same year, these men—delegates to represent their colonies in Congress—would adopt the Declaration of Independence? How did so many people change their mind in only a few months? How did they go

from loyal British subjects to defiant traitors and rebel Patriots?"

"That's a big jump in a short amount of time," Emily said. "I bet the war made people mad. The redcoats taking over Boston and shooting at their militias was already happening. What else had changed?" Emily knew she was onto something when Fred pointed his finger at her and smiled.

"You got it. Something did change. First, Congress received a response to the Olive Branch Petition."

"It wasn't good, was it?" Ethan said, with a mouth full of cookie.

"Nope. King George wouldn't even read the letter. Instead, he issued a proclamation of rebellion—that all colonists in open arms and all members of the Continental Congress should be captured and hanged. Next thing they knew, ships full of Hessians started coming to shore," Fred said.

"Well, that escalated quickly," Emily rolled her eyes. "I bet John Dickinson and the other conservatives were a little shocked." She dunked half of a cookie in her glass of milk. "Now they were seen as traitors, whether they liked it or not."

"All of this was undeniable proof that the King didn't see the colonists as citizens but as unruly rabble to be controlled," Fred concluded.

Ethan bumped his fist on the desktop, just enough to make the glasses and plates vibrate. "Everything you've taught us so far—the Age of Exploration, the Renaissance, the Protestant Reformation, the Glorious Revolution of 1688, and the tax protests—those all started with ideas. That's how all revolutions start through history," he said. "So *someone* has to start talking!"

More About Us!

John Dickinson
Pennsylvanian conservative

A key member of the Stamp Act Congress and prominent Pennsylvania legislator, Dickinson published 12 essays called *Letters from a Pennsylvania Farmer* from 1767 to 1768. They were widely read in all the colonies, uniting the people against the Townshend Acts. Influenced by his Quaker upbringing, he refused to sign the Declaration of Independence but later joined the fight once independence had been declared.

Patrick Henry
Virginian liberal

Possibly the most daring of the Founding Fathers, Patrick Henry was often the very first to take action. From his Virginia Resolves that spurred the Stamp Act revolt, to the Gunpowder Incident, to his infamous speech at the Virginia convention, Henry lived by this conviction: "Give me liberty or give me death!"

He drafted the Virginia State Constitution and became the state's first governor after signing the Declaration of Independence.

"A few brave people *did* speak out, but not many," Fred said.

"Patrick Henry, for instance," Emily said, holding up a card. "It says he was a Virginian radical, and one of the first to publicly call for a war for independence from Britain."

"You were right, Fred," Ethan said. "Virginia really is the baking powder in the continental cookies."

"Oh, just you wait!" Fred replied. "There's one more Virginian to talk about. But first, something else from the baking soda—Pennsylvania."

"Benjamin Franklin, I bet," Ethan said. "He seems to have his fingers in everything."

Fred burst into unexpected laughter, surprising even himself. "He really did!" Fred picked up the card with the older looking man with long, gray hair on the sides and a bald spot on the top. "Everyone knows that he was a genius inventor and discovered that lightning was static electricity. But most don't know that he was the royal postmaster for all the colonies, which back then was one of the highest positions one could have. He also spent most of his time in London in counsel with Parliament and the King's officers. I'd say he was the most influential colonist at the time. So whichever way he went, many people would follow."

"So what did he do this time?" Emily asked. "Hopefully the right thing."

"Let's go back two years, to 1774," Fred replied. "After the Boston Tea Party, Parliament instituted the Intolerable Acts. It was a horrible and cruel response. Franklin even tried to pay for the tea out of his own pocket, remember? But they didn't care about that. They only cared about punishment and control. By then, Franklin knew there was no use trying to bargain with Parliament."

"It was at this time that he was introduced to a brilliant young man who was ill and down on his luck," Fred said, pausing for emphasis. "His name was Thomas Paine."

"I know that name," Emily said. "I just saw it on an old book on that shelf."

"Will you please go get it for me?" Fred asked.

"Franklin put Paine on a boat to Philadelphia with a letter of recommendation," he continued, as Emily got up to fetch the book. "A letter from Benjamin Franklin back then was a sure ticket to get a job. Paine barely survived the voyage. He almost died of scurvy! But with the care of Franklin's personal doctor, he regained his strength and immediately got work as editor of the *Pennsylvania Magazine*, writing articles about human rights, abolishing slavery, and other radical liberal ideas. The magazine became the most popular magazine in the colonies."

"I'm a little confused why a Tory… a 'conservative' like Benjamin Franklin, would help a radical liberal like Thomas Paine start a revolution," Emily said.

"I'd like to know that too," Ethan added.

Fred stopped for a moment to think. Instead of answering, he took out a pen and wrote the question on a napkin, folded it, and put it in his shirt pocket. "Ask me again *after* the war is over."

Ethan took the awkward silence as a cue to finish his cookie and take another. "Did Paine's magazine make people want a war for independence?"

"Ethan, If he had written about that, he would have been arrested for treason," Emily said.

"You're absolutely right," Fred said, taking the book from her. "This little book is called *Common Sense*. This edition was printed later, but when it was first published in January of 1776, Paine didn't even put his name on it. It was anonymous—the writer's identity was hidden. To his surprise, Paine's first printing sold out. Then his second. He ended up printing 120,000 copies, and it sold out over and over. More people read his pamphlet than any other piece of writing, except the Bible."

"What did the book say?" Emily asked, munching on her second cookie. They were sweet and chewy but also buttery and a little crispy—precisely the way she liked them.

Fred took a sip of his milk. "It had quite a lot to say about the King."

"Oh! Yeah!" Ethan said. "Everyone thought the King was holy, that God wanted him to be their ruler, so anything anyone did against the King was against God, too."

"But Paine said that was nonsense," Fred replied. "Kings only had power because the people supported them. His authority came by his honor. If kings did wrong, breaking their honor, then Paine argued that the people had a right to break away from them."

"That's bold," Emily said.

"Especially in his time," Fred acknowledged. "These ideas took the country by storm. All of a sudden, there were lots of people thinking not just about getting respect and representation, but about being totally free from British rule altogether. Even many Tories and loyalists were forced to finally accept this reality. They had to fight back. They had to become independent."

"It's weird that he was a Brit," Emily said. "I thought the British were all against the Patriots."

"Not even close," Fred said. "There were many thousands of people in Britain who wanted the Crown to treat the colonies better. One man, John Wilkes—"

Emily jumped to her feet. "He was the one who shot President Lincoln!"

Fred laughed. "You're about a hundred years too early. That was John Wilkes *Booth*, who was an American, not a Brit, and who wasn't born until about sixty years after the events we're talking about. But he was named after this particular John Wilkes, who was a Whig leader and a radical liberal in England. He became mayor of London and a newspaperman. He wrote a series of sensational articles about the first battles of the war, and here's the shocker—he wrote them as if the British were in the wrong."

The twins were surprised. "Wouldn't he get in trouble for that?" Emily said.

"Yes. Wilkes and other Whigs were accused of inciting the war, which might have been true in Wilkes's case. He had been secretly writing letters to radical liberal leaders in the colonies for years, encouraging them in their protests. Even though King George III and the Tories were in control now, Wilkes and the Whigs still had many supporters in England, and they encouraged an end to the taxes, and an end to the Intolerable Acts, and an end to sending more redcoats and Hessians to fight them. They listened to the colonists and wanted to treat them as citizens."

More About Us!

John Wilkes   1725 – 1797

This crass, Scottish parliamentarian was gaining mass celebrity status for his radical political views, his libertine merriment, and his treasonous publications. He was a member of multiple clubs, including the secretive Hellfire Club, where he may have known Benjamin Franklin. He would often spend time with the drunken rabble in London's taverns, hence his popularity and political invincibility. To indulge himself in drink and intellectual discussions, he joined the Headstrong Club that gathered weekly at the White Horse Tavern. It was there he met the frustrated Thomas Paine, whose marriage and career had recently fallen apart.

Benjamin Franklin   1706 - 1790

In the course of his life, he was a successful writer, scientist, inventor, entrepreneur, postmaster general, and influential colonial representative in London, spending much of his time there. He affiliated with many groups, including the Freemasons and the irreverent Hellfire Club, where he associated with high ranking politicians and the London elite, perhaps including the radical liberal John Wilkes. It may have been as a result of these connections that he changed from being a prominent Tory to a liberal revolutionary who became a key figure in the fight for the independence of the American colonies, even helping draft the Declaration of Independence.

Thomas Paine   1737 - 1809

Intellectually curious, Paine joined a discussion group called the Headstrong Club. There he befriended John Wilkes. Paine's liberal spirit was radicalized by Wilkes's revolutionist ideas. Through another associate, Paine was introduced to Benjamin Franklin. He enticed Paine to move to the American colonies—paying for his travel, medical care, and guaranteeing him work as a political writer. Within a few years, Paine became the most influential writer in the colonies, driving public opinions about the abolition of slavery, workers' rights, and the overthrow of the British monarchy. Years later, he would help start the French Revolution.

But What Is Freedom?

Ethan rubbed his chin. "Governments were often treating people like slaves, but thanks to Paine's writings people are starting to look for another way— like not having a king at all. But look at these cards. These delegates had very different ideas about what a better government should be."

"Liberals believed that prosperity and happiness came from free trade and individual rights. But conservatives believed it was the power of government that provided order and safety," Emily explained.

Fred leaned forward. "So which were good guys, and which were bad guys?"

Ethan reached out for the stack of blue cards. He was going to point to the liberals, but then pulled his hand back. "They all were trying to do what they thought was right," he finally said. "For example, there's—wait, where is he?"

Emily passed a red card over. "Is this the one you want?"

"Yes! John Dickinson! He was the one who sent out the Olive Branch Petition. He knew fighting against the government was going to create chaos and hurt people. He wanted to return to order and peace."

"But King George only wanted control. He *wasn't* making peace. So I think the liberals were right—they shouldn't be loyal to a government that doesn't respect their liberty and rights," Emily said. "But those differences don't matter anymore. The Continental Congress is ready to fight for independence. They're Patriots now."

Fred blew out a long breath. "Yes. They're going to fight *against* the King, But what purpose are they fighting *for*?"

Emily tapped at the cards on the desk. "Independence."

"That's right. Freedom," Ethan said.

"Is independence the same thing as freedom?" Fred asked.

There was a long silence, broken only by the ticking of a clock on a nearby shelf.

"No," Emily said, at the exact same time Ethan said, "Yes."

All three of them broke up laughing.

Fred finally said, "Well, that's a problem, isn't it? Independence will give them freedom from the King, but will they really be more free under a different government? Should a government be very strong to protect rights, or very limited so it can never abuse its power and infringe on the people's rights?"

"That's a hard question," Emily said, thinking out loud.

"One thing was for sure, though, these treasonous Patriots needed a place to figure out the answer," Fred said, standing up to leave. "And write a declaration for their revolutionary ideas."

"The Declaration of Independence!" Ethan said, throwing a card down. "Thomas Jefferson—the other Virginian!"

"The Continental Congress is back in session!" Emily said, grabbing the last cookie.

Fred showed them to the door. "When you see me next, I'll explain how that revolutionary document changed the world!"

A Thought From Elijah

I think there were a *lot* of people before Thomas Paine started writing who knew that a king was just a spoiled, silly guy in a ridiculous costume. They didn't believe there was anything magical about his proclaimed authority to rule over others, but they went through their days keeping their mouths shut. They were afraid to speak the obvious truth.

People in power will always want you to feel afraid to speak the truth. Here's why: a courageous person who speaks the truth is the most dangerous thing to a tyrant—because once one person says it, others find the courage to say it as well. If you're that courageous person, pretty soon you may find that almost everyone is on your side.

Let's Talk About It!

Few of us, if any, like to be controlled by others. But it's not enough for us to simply desire an increase in freedom; we have to assume responsibility for ourselves and others.

Think of the colonists as they assembled in Congress and worked toward independence. They had been experimenting with self-governance for a long time and had grown accustomed to taking care of themselves. They were prepared to be free because they were willing to take responsibility for themselves and their community.

Children also want more freedom; it's tempting to see how "free" adults are and want the same opportunities. We don't like when our parents put restrictions on us and prevent us from doing what we want. So if more freedom comes with an increase in responsibility, what are some things that you can do to demonstrate to your parents that you're ready for more freedom? Come up with some ideas and talk to them about it!

Chapter 11
Liberty For All

A Day of Celebration or Resentment?

The twins couldn't remember if the sky had ever been so blue. The clouds were puffy and white, and a gentle breeze kept the temperature perfectly comfortable. It was as though nature was just as excited about the Independence Day parade as the Tuttles were.

Ethan and Emily had staked out the perfect spot and spread their blankets long before the first floats arrived. They both had empty bags in-hand, ready to be filled with lots and lots of the famous Spoonerville parade candy. Their parents sat on lawn chairs behind them, chatting with Mr. and Mrs. Lopez. The twins saw Maddox nearby, sitting with his mother. He had painted a red, white, and blue star on his cheek. They waved to each other.

Then the sounds that they had all been waiting for arrived: sirens, drums, horns, the tramp of horses, and hundreds of marching feet. There were candidates running for office, an Adventure Scout troop, and other parade floats advertising local businesses. The floats were all decorated differently, but they did have one thing in common. Candy!

Ethan looked down the street toward the source of music that was growing louder—a white truck pulling a trailer stacked with straw bales was blasting "Take Me Out to the Ball Game" from its speakers. Sitting on the bales were the regional Little League Champions—the same team that had defeated Ethan and Emily earlier that summer. Ethan looked over at Emily. Maybe their team could have been in the parade if he had followed her signal not to steal third base. Emily glanced back and smiled, letting Ethan know that it wasn't that important to her anymore.

The parade watchers began to rise to their feet, in linear sequence, making a wave like the crowds did at the Tigers' football games. The reason for the stir was the flag of the United States passing by, carried reverently by a few military veterans. Behind them came ranks of uniformed men and women. Their faces were like stone, their eyes fixed on the American flag.

Emily had a catch in her throat. So many soldiers! Some were wounded. She saw a woman missing an arm, and the last rows of soldiers rolled themselves down the street in their wheelchairs. The marching

band played the national anthem, slowly, with real feeling, marching at a quiet pace behind the uniforms ahead of them.

Ethan felt the swell of emotion that was now radiating from his community. His heart beat faster as he watched everyone standing together unified. Some faces even had tears trickling down, but those same people also had so much pride that their chests puffed out. When the police cars went by, lights flashing, but sirens silent, the whole parade route held its breath.

And then, without enough warning, the marching band changed songs, blasting out "Celebration." The party continued, as did the wild distribution of candy that flew like hail in a spring storm. There were feathers and streamers and rock bands and cheerleaders—a true celebration of American independence.

Just as the twins were scooping up another handful of candy and shoving it into their already bulging bags, a different kind of float came by.

It was an older car, surrounded by black-shirted marchers. They didn't yell or scream. They didn't cheer, or sing, or play any music at all. They just walked.

Each one carried a sign. But they weren't patriotic signs. They said, "Colonizers," "Slavery," "Genocide," "American fascism," and other such things. Their faces were grim. Alongside them, more marchers walked along the edge of the street handing out flyers. Emily took one from a Native American lady. She looked at it.

It was a history timeline, but the usual things Emily expected to see were not there. Instead, the flyer showed a long list of dates and terrible events that happened. Slaves being sold. Treaties being broken. The Trail of Tears. The first slave ships.

Many people refused to take the flyers. Some crumpled them up and threw them back, littering the road. A few even heckled the marchers, calling them ungrateful and unpatriotic.

"Go live in another country if you don't like it," one man yelled. Several people cheered in agreement.

Emily looked over at Maddox and his mother. They had stepped away from the road a bit, and didn't take a flyer, but they kept their eyes fixed on the marchers. One of the marchers looked back at them and nodded.

together, now some of them were quite sad. Mr. Lopez shook his head and then left with their children and bags toward the parking lot, while Mrs. Lopez began to pack up their blanket and chairs.

Ethan saw her struggle with all of the items and ran over to help. Mrs. Lopez was grateful for the gesture, but her faint smile struggled to break through her strong emotions. She handed the blanket to Ethan and he walked with her to her car. When he came back, his face was sad.

"She seemed really bummed out by what happened," Ethan said. "It's pretty sad that some people are still focused on being so divisive and causing problems."

Emily saw the crowd, bunched up in little knots here and there, people keeping to themselves. "The more things change, the more they stay the same, I guess."

"You two ready to go to the park?" Mrs. Tuttle asked. Mr. Tuttle had already packed up their chairs and bags.

"Sounds good!" Ethan said, popping a piece of bubble gum in his mouth.

"I'm a little bit sick of eating candy," Emily said. "I'm ready for some of Mom's chicken salad."

Ethan blew a bubble. "I'm always ready for a picnic lunch!"

Emily read the flyer, then folded it in half and slipped it into her back pocket.

After the marchers passed, the crowd's cheerful holiday mood had decreased. There were still many floats, and people cheered and tried to get back into the spirit of celebrating Independence Day, but they didn't have much success. Even the bright sun seemed to be a little less warm, as if a cloud had covered it.

Where once the whole community had been chatting and laughing and cheering

The Shameful History

When the crowds of people streamed away from the parade route, they seemed subdued, as if some of the original fun of the day had blown away in the light breeze. But the park was packed with people barbecuing, playing on playground equipment, and lying on the shores of the river. There were several food trucks—those were always a great sight. Plus music, bands, and lots of games like horseshoes and volleyball. The festival was far from over.

The Tuttles had a special spot they liked, not far from a huge oak tree that gave shade to the whole area. So many people had come to the park that the Tuttles had to park blocks away. But for Emily, that was okay. She felt like walking, but the flyer that was still folded in her pocket felt bulkier and crinkled more loudly than it should have. She just couldn't take her mind off of it.

She watched the people as they walked. Some of them had been at the parade. A few others Emily recognized as having been *in* the parade. They were all sorts of people—some of them Asian, others clearly African or Latino, and others' ancestral origins weren't as clear. There were so many shades of skin color and hair. Honestly, she had never paid that close attention before. It was the incident that morning, and the information on the

flyer, that spurred those thoughts in her. But still, all the people seemed happy, glad to be sharing the park in celebration. Her mood lifted.

It seemed everyone in town was there, trying to have a good time with their families. The Tuttles noticed that there was a family that had taken their special spot, already spread out next to the tree.

"Oh no," Mrs. Tuttle said. "It looks like we're too late for where we wanted to sit."

But when they got closer, they saw that they knew the family. "Oh, it's the Miners!" Mr. Tuttle said. "Maybe they'll be willing to share the spot."

The Miners saw the Tuttles coming and waved to them to join them. The Tuttles strode across the grass, dodging a pack of children playing tag.

"You found our favorite spot in the park," Mr. Tuttle called out to them. "Great minds think alike?" he smiled.

Mr. Miner sat up to welcome them. "There's room if you'd like to join us. The tree has plenty of shade to offer!"

"And I'll bet you made your famous chicken salad, didn't you?" Mrs. Miner said to Mrs. Tuttle.

"Of course," Mrs. Tuttle replied. "But too much, I think."

"No such thing," Mr. Miner said, standing to help the Tuttles get set up. "I can eat your chicken salad all day."

"Are you sure?" Mrs. Tuttle said. "You were here first. It's your spot. We don't want to intrude on your plans."

"Look at it like a trade. We give some of our space under the tree in exchange for the best chicken salad in town," Mrs. Miner said. "And I brought a chocolate cake that is about ten times what we need. We can all share."

The shade under that particular tree was especially good. It really was the perfect spot, with the rest of the park spread out in front of them. Across the footpath on the amphitheater stage, rock music

blared from a local band. Ethan took off his shoes and stretched out. He usually didn't like having so many people around, but today it felt good to have everyone in town together to celebrate.

It was about ten minutes later that he realized he hadn't seen his sister in a while.

"Mrs. Miner," he said, "have you seen Emily?"

"She was just here," Mrs. Miner said. "We'll go look for her. You stay. Maybe you can play cornhole with your dad."

They didn't have to walk far. Over against a neighboring tree, they found Emily sitting, looking at the flyer. They called out to her, but Emily didn't respond. They walked closer.

Emily noticed Mrs. Miner and her husband approaching. "Is this stuff true?"

She handed them the flyer. On it was the list of terrible things that the Miners read slowly.

"Yes," Mrs. Miner said. "Yes, these things are true."

Emily's face scrunched up. "How can we still feel pride in America when we have done these terrible things in history? Mrs. Miner, you're a black woman, and Mr. Miner, you're Native American. People that look like me did these things to you. But you're still here celebrating? Why?"

The Miners looked at each other, and seemed to smile sadly. They sat down next to her on the grass, one on each side.

"Yes, we're here celebrating. Because this country's founding principles are worth celebrating. Even with the horrible things that happened—and they *were* horrible—it's still worth taking a moment to celebrate what was good."

"I don't understand that," Emily said. She looked miserable. "How can you celebrate, or our other friends, like Maddox or the Lopezes? How can we even be friends after what the European colonists did to your ancestors, just because their skin and culture were different?"

Mrs. Miner spoke so softly Emily could barely hear over the music from across the park. "Are you going to do terrible things to me?"

Emily's mouth dropped open. "Of course not!"

"Are any of these other people? Most of them are white."

"No, I don't think so." In fact, just at that moment, another family walked by and waved cheerfully to the Miners, who waved back.

"Why not?" Mrs. Miner asked. "After all, I'm black, as you said. Why not hate me?"

"Because... well, because that's terrible," Emily said. "You're a person. The color of your skin doesn't matter to me."

"Exactly," Mr. Miner said. "But the question is, where did you learn that? How did you learn it?"

Emily tried to think. She couldn't remember. "I don't think... I mean, no one

taught me that. It's just... obvious."

Mr. Miner laughed. "It's self-evident, right?" he said, winking at his wife.

"Indeed," Mrs. Miner said.

Just then the music stopped, and a voice said over the loudspeaker, "Gather around, folks. We have a special guest to introduce."

The Miners got up. "Let's go see who the guest is," Mrs. Miner said. She reached down to pull Emily up to her feet. Her hand was warm and friendly. Mr. Miner put one arm around Emily and pulled her close for a reassuring hug. It helped.

"I don't want to go," Emily said. "I want to keep talking about this."

"But this guest *will* keep the conversation going," Mrs. Miner said. "Come on."

The Declaration

On stage were three boys dressed as Continental soldiers, playing on their fifes. They stopped and bowed, and out from behind them came Thomas Jefferson, played by a familiar face. It was Fred, dressed in a colonial costume and wig!

He waved to the crowd. Most people cheered, but some booed him, and Emily just felt miserable. The flyer had said Jefferson was a slave owner. She couldn't cheer for someone like that.

Fred held up his hands for quiet, and began to speak. "I can understand that some of you aren't glad to see me. You know that I was not a perfect person. You know that I even owned slaves. And that was wrong. There's no denying that."

There was some applause. Fred went on. "But I ask you to think about what we're celebrating here today. Prosperity. Equality. Freedom. And I ask you to think about how we have those things, when never in history did they exist to such a degree."

Emily could see that people were thinking about it. She was, too.

"What was the world like before the United States? It was awful. Most people lived in abject poverty—never having enough food to be healthy."

"Ruthless kings reigned in terror over their subjects," he continued. "The never-ending wars of empires spread misery and slavery to all corners of the earth. People killed each other over resources, over religious differences, and even just for looking differently and speaking a different language."

"Then something began to change all that—a document that changed our world forever," Fred emphasized. "The Declaration of Independence."

Fred unfurled a scroll and began to read. "We hold these truths to be self-evident, that all men are created equal. That they are endowed by their Creator with certain unalienable rights, that among these are life, liberty, and the pursuit of happiness."

Now when he paused, the cheering was much louder. Emily clapped her hands. That was what she wanted. But America hadn't lived up to those words. Had it?

"Pursuing these ideas is why we've experienced greater peace and prosperity than any other time in history. So we must cherish these ideas and protect them above anything else. Yes," Fred said, bowing his head, "even when we failed to live up to them... when I failed to live up to them. That doesn't make the words untrue. It just means we

have to work harder to make them true every day."

Now the cheering was loud, and long. Emily saw some uniformed military veterans up toward the stage, reaching up to shake Fred's hand.

Emily turned to go, and there was Ethan. He took the flyer out of her hand. "Thomas Jefferson owned 600 slaves," he said, reading. "We can't just ignore that, right?"

Mr. Miner waved his hand at them to walk with him. "No, we shouldn't ignore that. In fact, we have to remember it. But then what? That's the big question.

People make an error when they just want to learn *about* history. But what's really important is what we learn *from* history—not just learn what *they* did, but what *we* need to do about it today. So let's start with what Fred just said about history. What was it like before the Declaration of Independence?"

Ethan said, "Bad. Poverty. War."

"And slavery for as far back as we know," Emily said.

"Did those things go away as soon as the Declaration was signed?"

The twins shook their heads.

"Of course it didn't. My ancestors, and the ancestors of my wife, were captured, enslaved, and killed. Some of that is still in the world today, but much less than before. Why are things better now?"

"Fred said it was because of the ideas in the Declaration," Ethan said, "but I don't understand how."

"Thomas Jefferson wrote that these truths are self-evident, which means they're super obvious. All people are born as equals. All of us should be able to live our lives peacefully, the way we want, without another person claiming they deserve to control us. Do you believe that?"

Ethan said, "Of course. No one should be allowed to hurt me or control me, and no one should be allowed to take my things or stop me from living my life in peace. I don't know how anyone could seriously believe otherwise."

Emily's face brightened. "It's self-evident! That's what you were saying before."

Mrs. Miner chimed in. "And that is why governments exist—to help protect these rights of life, liberty, and our pursuit of happiness from others who would try to kill us, enslave us, or stop us from living our best life, on our own terms."

Mr. Miner could tell Ethan was thinking extra hard about something. "Seems like you have another question. What is it?"

"Well, if the government was made to *protect* our rights, why is the government also one of the things that is most *threatening* to our rights?" Ethan asked.

He continued, "Politicians are always trying to control people, hurt others, and take our money. They don't act like our equals. They act like rulers." Ethan crossed his arms, and his brows furrowed a bit.

Emily said, "And look at this flyer! They wrote the words, but our nation hasn't lived by them. Even George Washington and Thomas Jefferson had hundreds of slaves! These truths must not be so self-evident after all."

"You're absolutely right," said a voice behind them. They turned, and there was Fred, taking off his powdered wig. He was sweating in his wool colonial outfit. "It's easy to listen to those words and agree with them, but when it comes to applying them in the real world, it can be more difficult and scary. Fear will make people lose faith in practicing those same principles we all believe to be true."

"Like the way some Founding Fathers treated the people they enslaved and the natives who were already here. They didn't respect their rights," Mrs. Miner said. "Fine speech, Fred."

"Thank you. It was hard work. I knew there were some in the crowd who might not listen. But the words still have to be said."

Mr. Miner shook Fred's hand. "So for a long time things didn't get a lot better for people like me," he added. "But these ideas had never really been tried before."

Fred nodded. "Did you know Thomas Jefferson even wrote a part in the Declaration of Independence that talked about the evils of slavery?"

Their faces quickly revealed their surprise. "No! Read us that part!" Emily said.

"I can't. It was taken out. Representatives from Georgia and South Carolina refused to join the fight against Great Britain if it wasn't removed, and if that happened they couldn't have won the fight for independence. Many people were so ignorant and arrogant that they believed their slaves were less than human, and they also feared that if they let them go, the slaves would attack them in revenge."

"The truth is that Jefferson was a product of his time, and raised in a culture where all of this was normal and expected," Fred continued. "It's rather unfair to judge people in the past by our present understanding of the world. But Jefferson was never really a fan of slavery—he treated his slaves well enough, and wrote often about how the practice should be ended. And freeing his slaves might mean they could be captured and enslaved by others who would treat them far worse."

"This flyer doesn't say anything like that," Emily said curiously.

"That flyer has facts, but isn't complete," Mr. Miner said. "It's propaganda."

More About This!

Thomas Jefferson & the Tradition of Slavery

Jefferson's plantation home, Monticello, Virginia

- Even though he kept six hundred people of African ancestry in slavery throughout his life, he was a public opponent of the institution.

- His wife, Martha, and many of his children died. Sally Hemmings, an enslaved woman, bore six children, who many believe were fathered by him; he freed them upon reaching adulthood. He might have kept the relationship a secret, as it was illegal to marry interracially until 1967.

- He believed that the institution of slavery was the greatest threat to the survival of the new American nation. He was right.

- He feared that if slavery was abolished, freed slaves would turn on their former masters for revenge.

- He was concerned about whether harmony could exist between races, so he proposed that a colony be set up for freed slaves.

- As governor of Virginia, he drafted a plan for the gradual abolition of slavery, though in some cases these measures unintentionally made the situation worse.

Emily had a light bulb moment. "We learned about that when Mrs. Miner took us to hear John Taylor Gatto speak."

"That's right. And what did he say propaganda was?" Mrs. Miner asked.

"When information is left out in order to paint an inaccurate story," Ethan said.

"And why would anyone want to do that?" Fred asked. The three adults were pressing the twins like it was the speed round of a trivia game show, but the twins could handle it.

Emily shot back, "It's to trick people into supporting something, or someone, that they otherwise wouldn't." The adults nodded approvingly.

"So you see, young friends," Fred added, "the publishers of that flyer are framing history in such a way as to make people feel angry, fight, and even hate themselves and others."

Emily thought about her own feelings. She'd been ashamed about her heritage and her race, and even questioned her own friendships. How could she have been tricked into feeling that way?

Mrs. Miner rested her hand on Emily's shoulder. "Because you're a good person, you felt sad and angry about that terrible history. People are more easily controlled with emotions. If others can influence your emotions, they can change what you think. Then they can change what you believe and how you vote and act. It's classic propaganda, and it all starts with bending the truth."

"But beware," Fred said, "propaganda comes from all sides of politics. Shallow history that makes you feel only happy and proud about your country, and that history was only 'good guys against bad guys,' will lead you to learn the wrong lessons too. It is just as deceitful, manipulative, and dangerous. Most of the 'history' taught in school, on TV and movies, and in books, has a political agenda designed to influence what you think and how you act."

"I guess I need to be more careful," Emily said. "Understanding the truth seems like it can be complicated."

"I like to know all the facts," Ethan said. "That's why I like how you teach, Fred. You're not afraid to tell us all the details."

Mr. Miner patted Fred on the shoulder. "That's the way all history should be taught, if you ask me. We can't really learn from history by pretending some things didn't happen. We shouldn't be afraid to talk about it."

Mrs. Miner looked at the twins with a gentle smile. "It's true that my ancestors were slaves and Mr. Miner's

ancestors were killed and driven off their lands not too long after these words were written—even by some of the same people who did heroic things that we praise. And that's a very sad thing."

"But it's also true that the ideas in the Declaration of Independence are what eventually freed my family," she added. "For the first time in history, people saw that slavery was evil and courageously fought to end it. That's also part of American history, and that's something to be very proud of."

The group ended up back under the shade of the big oak. Mr. and Mrs. Tuttle had set out the picnic and were ready to eat a feast of chicken salad, potato chips, and a tray of veggies.

Fred smiled even bigger than he usually did. "I'm so pleased with you two. Don't be afraid of the truth—take the good and the bad and learn from it. If you do that, I think you'll come to the same conclusion that I have... that all men really *are* created equal, and we must never be afraid to stand up for the rights of our fellow humans at all times and in all matters. Then politicians and their propaganda lose their power, and our world will continue to grow more peaceful, unified, and prosperous."

Liberty Can Unite Us

Later that night, most of the neighborhood gathered in front yards up and down the Tuttles' street. Mrs. Wakinona played music on her portable speaker. It was the perfect evening—except the kids couldn't wait for the sun to go down so the fireworks could start!

It was a good thing no one was out driving, because they could never have gotten through. The road was choked with people chatting, catching up, and neighbors celebrating the shared heritage that brought them together.

Emily thought about how cool that was. Even though there were bad things in

history, everyone seemed to be putting them aside and enjoying the good things instead. Wouldn't that make more of the good things? Emily thought it would.

But she remembered the marchers from the parade, too. She wished they could see what was happening on her block. They had been sad and angry— and maybe they had good reasons. Not everywhere was like this. There were still places where people were looked down on because of their skin color or because of where they were born. And that was wrong. How could this neighborhood party expand to include everyone? How could liberty and justice really become for all?

Fred wandered over, munching a hot dog. "Penny for your thoughts," he said.

"How can Americans become united, like the colonists were?" Emily said.

Fred chewed thoughtfully for a moment. He swallowed and said, "I think we *are* united as much as the colonists ever were, which is to say, they weren't."

"What?" Emily said. "I know before the Declaration, there were lots of debates. Not many people wanted independence from the British government. But after, didn't everyone get on board? Team America? All for one and one for all?"

Ethan came whizzing by, chasing after a frisbee. "That's the Three Musketeers," he said, teasing his sister.

"Still..." Emily said.

"No. Everyone most certainly did *not* get on board. Many Tories were still loyal to the crown and even fought alongside the Redcoats!"

Emily cocked an eyebrow.

More About Us!

William Franklin
1730–1813

Thomas Hutchinson
1711–1780

- The identity of his biological mother is unknown, as he was born of one of his father's affairs

- Assisted his father, Benjamin Franklin, in the famed kite experiment at the age of 21 years

- Appointed as the Royal Governor of New Jersey in 1763

- Was imprisoned by Patriot forces and held until he was released in a prisoner trade

- He organized spies and guerrilla militia from New York, fighting on the British side

- After the war, he fled to Britain, returning only once to reconcile with his dying father

- The great-great-grandson of Anne Hutchinson

- Was elected to a lifetime of high ranking political offices starting at the age of 26

- With the local currency struggling, he used his influence to outlaw an alternative money system developed by Samuel Adams's father

- Was the lieutenant governor and governor during the turmoil leading up to the revolution; was hated by the rebels for implementing the Crown's abusive actions

- Fled to England and died soon after

"Only about half of the colonists—the Patriots—were excited about the Declaration. Another quarter of the colonists—the loyalists—were totally opposed to it."

"What about the last quarter?"

"The rest felt it just wasn't worth taking a side. They figured the best way to stay safe was to stay quiet and out of the way," Fred explained.

"But then…" Emily began, still looking over the smiling, laughing neighborhood.

"That means the war wasn't just against the British. It was against… each other. Americans fighting other Americans who disagreed with them."

"Yes," Fred said. "The Revolutionary War was also a civil war—a war between family members and neighbors."

That might have been the saddest thing Emily had heard yet.

A minute later, Ethan came over to find Emily sitting on the curb. "We're getting sparklers," he said. "Come get one."

John Malcolm
?-1788

- Was an overzealous customs officer, loathed by most in Boston

- Seized two ships for not presenting the correct paperwork and insulted the crew, who poured tar and feathers on him and marched him through the streets

- After attacking a boy in the street, he beat a Son of Liberty with a cane, causing a serious head wound—prompting the crowd to tar and feather him and threaten to hang him

- Moved to England and ran for Parliament, unsuccessfully, against John Wilkes

Boston King
1760-1802

- Born a slave in South Carolina; became a master carpenter

- He joined the British when they occupied Charleston and promised him freedom

- In New York, he met and married Violet, a woman also from North Carolina, who was given an offer of freedom as well

- After the war, he and three thousand other black American slaves were given certificates of freedom

- He was evacuated to Nova Scotia, Canada, where he was appointed as Methodist minister to a congregation at Preston, near Halifax

Emily didn't move. The sun had set and the aerial fireworks would be starting soon. She then told Ethan what Fred had just taught her.

Ethan tried to imagine going to war against the Wakinonas. He couldn't. He quietly chuckled to himself instead.

"What's so funny?" Emily said. How could he be giggling thinking about this?

"Look at all these people. There's black and brown and tan and pink and everything. But they all eat and sleep and go to work. Some people like chicken and others like hot dogs. Some of them don't go to church and some do. We choose to live our lives differently. Can you imagine fighting about it?"

She couldn't.

"What if we wanted our neighbors to live just like us? Would we force them by getting the government to make laws?" Ethan asked.

"No way," Emily responded firmly.

"Now, what if *they* got the government to force us?" Ethan said. "Then would we fight them?"

"Maybe," Emily said. "But I would hope we'd just respect each other's rights to choose."

"Respect each other's pursuit of happiness?" Ethan added.

"Right, like the fact that we were all created equal, and that what you want for your life is just as important as what I want for mine. When we respect *that*, then there's nothing to fight about, no matter *what* our differences are."

Just then the first firework burst with a pop in the night sky. It was red, followed by a blue one, and then others of many colors.

From down the block, the speaker began to play "America the Beautiful." Whatever people were doing, they stopped to listen. And then they began to sing.

It wasn't great singing. But it was great. And more than a few faces were wet with tears. People had their arms around each other. Fred came up behind them.

"We read the words of the Declaration earlier, but this is what its ideas look like in practice. We're not perfect at it, but what's important is that we keep trying. Liberty for all."

"And crown thy good with brotherhood…" the neighborhood sang out.

Emily and Ethan found themselves singing along. "From sea to shining sea!"

A Thought from Connor and Elijah

This book is much different than the average history book. This book isn't a te-xtbook; we think it's better to tell stories. And these stories have lessons to offer us that we can learn from, including powerful ideas about how to create a freer world. Of course, it's these ideas that we can now put into practice in our day. That's the point of reading a book like this—to be inspired by past thinkers and doers and then ponder what we should think and do in our lives.

It's unfortunate, as we've seen, that so much history shows that when people want freedom and obtain power, they often use it to oppress others. Whether it was the Puritans enforcing their beliefs on those who disagreed or some of the founders who owned slaves despite preaching about freedom, imperfect people struggled in the past to live in accordance with what they claimed to believe. It's no different

today; as you get older you'll encounter plenty of people who say one thing but do another. It doesn't mean they disagree with the ideas—it just means that ideas are sometimes difficult to put into practice.

Think of this book as your starting point helping you learn about (and *from*!) events and people in our history. There are, frankly, so many important ideas and things that we simply couldn't cover. But what we did share here can inspire you to do your own research and continue learning with your family. There are hidden nuggets in history that await you!

Do you know what's *in* the Declaration? Understanding its ideas and their power is how we can learn *from* history and find opportunities to apply those ideas today. There is much to learn! So, what happens after independence was declared? We'll share more in Volume 2 of *America's History*!

Let's Talk About It!

Finding agreement is a difficult thing to do when people come from different backgrounds. Think of the colonists whose delegates in the Continental Congress debated the issue of independence. Many of them strongly disagreed on matters of religion, political authority, the use of power, and how free the market should be.

What ultimately united them was a common enemy—the British Empire. But agreeing on what you *oppose* does not lead to a lasting union. For that, you have to find agreement on things you *support*. We'll explore this in further detail in Volume 2 when we look at how the Founding Fathers debated this issue and explored how they could find consensus on what type of government they could all unify under and support.

It's a tricky topic, to be sure—because can diverse people ever really agree? If we go by majority rule, doesn't that mean there will always be a minority that doesn't get its way?

And what happens when the same people are in the minority over and over again... do they feel represented when their views are never agreed upon by others?

Too often, when people express a desire for unity, what they really want is *conformity*—making others think and act like they do. This typically involves using the government to force the majority's preferences on the minority, even though they don't agree.

How can you be unified with someone in your life who thinks very differently than you do? What's your social circle like? Are you only friends with people who are like you? Or do you also seek out and interact with people who have different ideas or interests?

The ultimate question is, does unity require conformity? What did Emily and Ethan discover together about how to be united with others who are different?

A Very Special Thanks

This book couldn't have happened without the support and assistance of some very important people who helped brainstorm, share ideas, check facts, develop stories, and more.

Murray Rothbard
Author, *Conceived in Liberty*

Chris Jones
Story contributor

Meghan Palmer
Story contributor

Patrick Newman
Historian consultant

Milo Stanfield
Illustration colorist

David Callihan
Historian consultant

Sergio Cariello
Title page illustrator

Justin Spears
Content contributor

Sponsor Recognition

This book was produced and distributed by Libertas Institute, an educational non-profit. We would like to express our gratitude to the following donors who helped fund this project.

The Draper Foundation
Sheldon and Cindy Stone
Chris Rufer
Daniels Fund

Sorenson Legacy Foundation
Conant Family Foundation
Considine Family Foundation

Jack Miller Family Foundation
Dick & Betsy DeVos Family Foundation
Rev Foundation

And the following additional supporters:

The Bride Family
Kacey McCoy
Kenneth Ellenberg
Michael King
Becky Moore
Daniel Richards
Ronald Cook
Patsy Ballard
Laura Kreuger
Ronald Nelson
Ramona Jones
Robin McCann
Gabrielle Lindbloom
Craig Young
Kim Wilson
Nicolette Moore
Jacob DeWitte
Don Cowles
Carl Liggio
Kacey McCoy
Michael Robichaux
Ted Uihlein
Jeff Alexander

Marilyn Woodhouse
Kathryn Funk
Michelle Chiba
Robert Hefner
Josiah Enyart
Julie Butler
John Peterson
Nikki Voss-Motes
Russell Lesser
John Harding
Gerald T Lee
David Campbell
John Van Scyoc
Ed & Amanda Ryan
Karen Carpenter
Richard Eitel
Joan Jones
Cathy Savino
Charles Garber
Willette & Manny Klausner
Judy Meitzler
Mary Jordan Saunders
Ryan Schudde

Betty Purtell
FM Wiley
Jami Satterthwaite
Carly and Charly
Donald G. Moore
James Dykes
Andy Anderson
Warren Davis
Luke Gambee
Mike Sheehan
Magalen Webert
Thomas Pryor
Scott Acker
Kathleen Lea
Alexander Cregier
John Bond
Joan Van Leeuwen
Jay Peters
Nancy Saenz
William Caldwell
John Olsen
Leslie Ochsner
Henry Miller